This project is supported by a grant from
The National Endowment for the Arts
in Washington, D.C., a Federal Agency

Printed in the United States of America

Contents

Officers and Members of the Council

150th Anniversary Exhibition Committee

Painters

DANIEL E. GREENE, NA

AARON SHIKLER, NA

Architects

WALKER O. CAIN, ANA

ROBERT S. HUTCHINS, NA

Sculptors

FRANK ELISCU, NA

MICHAEL LANTZ, NA

Graphic Arts

STEPHEN CSOKA, NA

HANS JELINEK, NA

Aquarellists

CHEN CHI, NA

MARIO COOPER, NA

ALFRED EASTON POOR, PNA, *ex-officio*

DANIEL CATTON RICH, *Guest Director of the Exhibition*

Foreword

The first President of the National Academy of Design, and one of the first fifteen founders, Samuel F. B. Morse, suggested using the word design in the title and, at that time, design included Painting, Sculpture, Architecture and Engraving. Now, one hundred and fifty years later, these arts, with the exception of Architecture, are taught in the School which the Academy maintains, and these same disciplines, including Architecture, as exemplified by Academicians and Associates, are shown in this our Retrospective Exhibition, "A Century and a Half of American Art."

The purpose of this Exhibition is to show the part played in the development of American Art and Architecture by members of the Academy, and to show the best or most interesting work of Academicians or Associates in the basic arts, whether from our own very extensive collection or borrowed from Museums and Private Collections. During the past four years in which we were planning for this Exhibition, we made extensive research into the background and history of the artists represented and the pertinent data about the works of art shown, which has enabled us to print this extensive catalogue which should be of interest to scholars and to the general public.

The selection of the Painting, Sculpture, Water Colors and the Graphic Arts in the Exhibition has been the responsibility of Daniel Catton Rich, in consultation with the Academy's Committees: Daniel E. Greene and Aaron Shikler for Painting; Frank Eliscu and Michael Lantz for Sculpture; Chen Chi and Mario Cooper for Water Color; and Hans Jelinek and Stephen Csoka for the Graphic Arts.

It is interesting to know that amongst the founders there were two Architects, Ithiel Town and M. E. Thompson. After these founders there were no Architects elected until Charles F. McKim in 1907, followed in the next few years by his partner, W. R. Mead and Cass Gilbert, John M. Carrère, Thomas Hastings and Charles A. Platt, a Landscape Architect as well as an Architect. The Co-Chairmen of the Architectural Committee, Walker O. Cain and Robert S. Hutchins and I, as an Architect, decided that as Architects' sketches, drawings and models are generally boring to the public, the Architectural Exhibit would consist of photographs of the outstanding buildings constituting the best work of the Architectural members of the Academy. These are all taken by the same Architectural Photographer, Alexandre Georges, one of the outstanding Architectural Photographers in this country. As all the buildings shown have been photographed during the past year, the photographs will show how well some of the older ones, with the patina of age added, have stood the test of time.

We are indebted to the Museum of the City of New York, and to its President, Louis Auchincloss, and Director, Joseph Veach Noble, for recreating one of our galleries into a room as it would have been in 1825, the year of our founding.

Our special thanks go to the Committees of the Academy formed for this Exhibition, to the Council of the Academy, and to the many Museums and Private Collectors who so generously have loaned Paintings, Graphics and Sculpture which, together with our own Collection, have enabled us to show the best work of deceased members. Our thanks also to Daniel Catton Rich for his discerning advice on the selection of the Painting and Sculpture in the Exhibition and for his skillful mounting of the show, and to George North Morris for his History of the Academy. And, most of all, our thanks and gratitude to Miss Alice G. Melrose, the Director of the Academy, for without her devoted and untiring help and advice, this Exhibition could never have taken place.

ALFRED EASTON POOR, NA
President

By Way of Introduction

December, 1975 marks the hundred and fiftieth anniversary of the founding of the National Academy of Design. To celebrate this occasion the National Collection of Fine Arts, Smithsonian Institution in Washington arranged this summer an exhibit, "Academy, the Academic Tradition in American Art," examining through art in historical detail the role played by the National Academy in the larger academic development in America from 1825 to the 1960s.[1]

The present exhibition in the Academy's New York galleries has a different intention. Its aim is to show a number of excellent works by members, stressing individual achievement in the fields of painting, sculpture, graphic arts, watercolor and architecture—those divisions in which the Academy operates. Both the Washington exhibit and ours rely heavily on works owned by the Academy. No other institution in the area of American art possesses so continuous a visual history by its members. From the first, when elected, each Associate was required to furnish a self-portrait or one done of him by another, and after 1840 when named an Academician, he was asked to contribute a further example of his art (the "diploma" piece). The result is a fascinating treasury of works by American artists, many of these little known to the public. The Academy's resources have been augmented by gifts of entire collections and by a number of individual works given by families of former members.

Before I was invited as guest director for the New York exhibition it had been decided not to show work by living Associates or Academicians but to represent the Academy through significant artists of its past. Committees in the various fields were appointed by the President to advise the director. I met with them and want to express appreciation for their suggestions, many of which have been followed in my selection. The architectural section, however, was assembled by its own committee which chose those architects and buildings to be included.

Our exhibition has been rounded out with loans from many museums and private collectors. I am especially grateful to them for realizing the importance of the occasion and for generously contributing superb works which, during a Bicentennial year, are greatly in demand. The intention, however, has not been to invite only masterpieces but to show at times a less familiar side of an artist. Instead of a striking portrait, George Bellows appears in a romantically charged landscape, "The White Horse" (lent by the Worcester Art Museum). The case of Bellows illustrates another point. It was decided in certain instances where a painter excelled in various media, to show him in more than one work. In the gallery given to the graphic arts you will find Bellows's macabre drawing, "Dance in the Madhouse" (lent by The Art Institute of Chicago) as well as his famous lithograph, "A Stag at Sharkey's" (lent by The Brooklyn Museum).

American sculpture came of age much later than American painting. Its small representation here reflects not only a practical limitation as to size and expense of transporting large (if not monumental) pieces. It presents a sample by some sculptors who worked during this period and who were often more lively, in my opinion, when they turned to smaller, more expressive works. Again the section of graphic arts shows a few of our best draughtsmen and printmakers and may be enjoyed for variety rather than for completeness. Only in 1943 did painters in watercolor become a separate category. This helps to explain the brevity of this group, though I readily admit it has been greatly enlivened by painters like Homer, Sargent, Eakins and Grosz, all shown in oils as well.

Since it was decided not to present a strict historical survey of art by Academicians and Associates from 1825–1975 (this having been splendidly done in Washington) what does the exhibit set out to do? It attempts to highlight some of the accomplishments of its most accomplished members. It further brings to the public's attention certain fascinating artists whose works have not been seen for many years. In borrowing from outside sources I have tried to keep in mind a balance between well known paintings, sculpture and prints and those seldom seen in New York.

Certain examples in the strictly academic vein have been included as well as more progressive works. Our reawakened interest in nineteenth century landscape and our tradition in portrait painting (both fields in which Members of the Academy excelled) have been given consideration. In short, within limitations of space and budget, the aim is to indicate the important, sustaining role of the National Academy of Design and to point with pride to the many masters who have joined, exhibited and supported an undertaking founded solely by artists and administered by them for a century and a half.

DANIEL CATTON RICH
Guest Director of the Exhibition

1. See the informative catalogue by Lois Marie Fink and Joshua C. Taylor, full of useful information on the Academy and its history.

The Tradition

Frustrated art students initiated the action which resulted in the formation of the National Academy of Design. Aspiring young artists Thomas Cummings and Frederick Agate arrived early one morning in 1825 at the door of the twenty-three-year-old American Academy of the Arts, then located in the old Alms House on Chambers Street opposite New York's City Hall. They had made several previous attempts to enter the Academy's rooms for the purpose of drawing from the collection of plaster casts of Greek and Roman antiquities and had decided to make a final assault on the then bastion of art in New York. Turned away again by the old keeper (who was later supported by the American Academy's prestigious president, elderly John Trumbull), Agate and Cummings conferred with the latter's teacher, Henry Inman, on what course of action to take.

The result was the first instance of cooperation among American artists for their own benefit. The American Academy of the Arts had been organized by a group of local businessmen-patrons, among whom was DeWitt Clinton. Their aim was to promote the cultural aspects of art in the community with little attention to the welfare of living artists. Artists were always in the minority on their board of directors. So the New York Drawing Association, formed as a result of the Agate-Cummings incident by thirty men whose sole purpose was to improve their drawing skill, was a landmark step in the development of American art. Among the group were some of this country's most important artists of the period: Samuel F. B. Morse (elected president), Henry Inman, Asher B. Durand, Hugh Reinagle, and Thomas Cole. The principal visual arts—painting, sculpture, engraving and architecture—were all represented among the membership. Ironically the room which the Drawing Association used was located in the same building in which the American Academy of the Arts occupied the second floor.

It had not been the intention of the Drawing Association to compete with the American Academy on any but the school level. However, a confrontation with the Academy, instigated by Trumbull's pompous demand that the Drawing Association members sign up as students of the Academy, impelled the Association to sever all connections with that institution (i.e. they returned a few borrowed casts) and reorganized themselves in January, 1826, as the National Academy of the Arts of Design. In two ballots of fifteen members each a nucleus of thirty artists were elected by the board of directors to form the National Academy.

The membership differed slightly from the Drawing Association. Among new members were Samuel Waldo and Rembrandt Peale. The first meeting of the National Academy of the Arts of Design was held at Morse's home on January 19, 1826, and the pioneer American art organization of, by, and for artists was officially on its way.

That same year a constitution for the new Academy was approved. In 1828 a charter was obtained from the State of New York, and rules for membership were established that have changed little in the intervening years. New York City residency requirements were eliminated in 1863. Similar to the framers of the United States Constitution itself, the organizers of the National Academy of Design had remarkable foresight concerning the real needs of artists in our society. Two of the requirements for membership as an Academician which were early instituted have had a salient effect in forming the Academy's excellent permanent collection of art, one of the largest collections of American art in this country. On the occasion of his election as an Academician each member must present an example of his work to the Academy. Also each Associate-elect, prior to 1973, contributed a portrait of himself, either by himself or by a fellow artist. This has become a visual record of American artists of the past 150 years of inestimable value.

One of the most important functions of the Academy as it developed was the opportunity it afforded artists to exhibit their work. The presence of too many amateurs among the exhibitors in the early years made a jury of selection a necessity for the annual exhibitions. The nature of the juries has changed over the years, but the jury system has maintained a general high quality of exhibits of benefit both to the reputation of the Academy and to the pleasure of the visiting public. Admission fees charged the public to the exhibitions were important in defraying the costs to the Academy, and the jury guaranteed visitors that they would get their money's worth.

The school, which was the outgrowth of the old original Drawing Association, has been one of the chief strengths of the Academy. Because the teachers have always been members of the Academy, the students were well introduced to the mysteries of the profession of art and provided a constantly enriching stream of new Academicians and Associates. Its initial session as the school of the National Academy was on November 15, 1826, in the rooms of the Philosophical Society in the Alms House with an enrollment of twenty students. The school moved as the Academy moved, but it was only after the Academy finally located in its "Doge's Palace" on the corner of Twenty-Third Street and Fourth Avenue in 1865 that it acquired the kind of spacious surroundings necessary for studying art. This lasted until the end of the century when growing pains again struck both the Academy and its school. Through the Nineteenth Century there was a see-saw fiscal theme which threaded its way through the tuition policies of the Academy. For the most part the aim of free tuition for all who could benefit from it—that is, based on talent alone—was realized, and this policy continued until 1950. In 1959 the new, half-million dollar, skylighted building, adjoining the Academy galleries on Eighty-Ninth Street at the corner of Fifth Avenue was opened. Since then the tuition fees have assured the students of thoroughly professional instruction. Instruction is offered in drawing, painting, sculpture, composition and graphic arts in morning, afternoon and evening sessions for all but about three weeks in the year. Many of America's major artists received their basic art instruction at the Academy, notably Winslow Homer, Albert Pinkham Ryder, William M. Chase, Augustus Saint-Gaudens, Charles Hawthorne, Arshile Gorky, Maurice Sterne, John Costigan, Ben Shahn, Adolph Gottlieb, Carl Holty and the three Soyer brothers. Students are aided by some thirty tuition grants in the form of merit, monitor or clerical scholarships and by more than $3500 in exhibition prizes annually.

In 1827, at the end of the Academy's first season, President Samuel F. B. Morse delivered an address on the occasion of the presentation of the first awards for excellence to students. This occurred in the chapel of Columbia College, then located at Church Street opposite Park Place, and resulted in the first real colloquy on the place of art and the academic idea in American society. An anonymous author in *The North American Review* scorned the presumption of using the name "National Academy" and, more caustically, minimized the position which art should occupy in this nation of science and industry. He was perhaps echoing the pronouncement of John Adams who wrote that his generation should study the arts of government so that their sons could study the arts of commerce so that their sons could study the arts of leisure. It might sound logical, but civilizations do not develop that way, and Morse and the Academy would have none of it. The upshot of the public discussion which followed was a strengthening of the Academy's position in New York, more lively support by the artists, and historical vindication of Morse's view that art is an integral part of every developing society.

The old American Academy, still alive and audible, was also drawn into the debate instigated by the writer in *The North American Review*. The resulting exchange of charges and counter charges contributed to the decline in prestige of John Trumbull and the American

Academy because the new National Academy had such an able spokesman in Morse. He was another example of the right man in the right place at the right time. The American Academy expired in 1841, and its remaining effects were auctioned off in the galleries of the National Academy. An ironic demise.

As the National Academy grew in numbers and influence, it became necessary to find new quarters about once a decade as facilities continually proved to be inadequate. From the Old Alms House the Academy moved successively to Clinton Hall in 1831, the Society Library in 1841, 663 Broadway in 1850, and temporary galleries on Tenth Street in 1857. During this time two able men, Morse and Asher B. Durand, had been leading the Academy as presidents through these years of flux. Morse returned for a brief stint as president in 1861–62. He was succeeded by one of the National Academy's most able administrators, Daniel Huntington, who helped shepherd the organization through perhaps its most important years of development. He presided from 1862 to 1870 and again from 1877 to 1891. His first major duty as president was to oversee the construction of the new Academy headquarters on Twenty-Third Street. It was expected that the nation's involvement with the Civil War would impede the erection of the new building, but the members were surprised beyond their fondest hopes when the means for constructing what became known familiarly as the "Doge's Palace" was quickly found in spite of the national unrest. Meade's win at Gettysburg and the Emancipation Proclamation were not the only events of importance to occur in 1863. On April 18th of that year President Huntington turned a shovelful of earth to start construction of the National Academy's first and only headquarters designed and built to house all of its activities under one roof. The corner stone laying on October Twenty-First was a grand affair. Speeches by Parke Godwin, Samuel F. B. Morse, William Cullen Bryant and historian George Bancroft guaranteed that the building would have an auspicious baptism.

It might be difficult to prove a direct connection, but the coincidence of the conclusion of the Civil War and the opening of the Academy's new headquarters in the same month of 1865 symbolized the kind of death-and-rebirth syndrome which seems to accompany all such upheavals. What followed was certainly a flowering for the Academy, just as the country itself embarked on an expansion unparalleled in history.

Before the Civil War the National Academy was just one of several organized attempts to promote art in the United States. Not only the American Academy, but the Apollo Association—which evolved into the hugely successful American Art-Union—the Düsseldorf

Gallery and the New York Gallery all made differing claims for the art public's attention. However, the aftermath of the war left the field to the National Academy alone. The organization had gained prestige by its unceasing activities on behalf of artists and art students. The expansion of the country and the consequent interest in landscape painting as a worthy art specialization, the newly acquired wealth of the industrial barons which necessitated the kind of legitimization which only commissioned portraits and art collections can bestow, and the increased foreign influence on American artists contributed to a previously unknown popularity and sophistication in both the public and the artists of the last third of the Nineteenth Century.

Since the National Academy was then the only agency through which artists could conveniently reach the public, membership grew. This was the period during which America's "Old Masters" developed. And most of them were members of the Academy: Thomas Eakins, Winslow Homer, Frank Duveneck, John Singer Sargent, Albert Pinkham Ryder and William Merritt Chase among the painters; Daniel Chester French, James Earle Fraser, Lorado Taft and Augustus Saint-Gaudens, sculptors; Timothy Cole, Charles Dana Gibson and Joseph Pennell, graphic artists; and Charles F. McKim, William R. Mead and Cass Gilbert, architects.

An additional advantage to the Academy which its hard won prestige accrued was the acquisition of a generous number of endowments around the turn of the Twentieth Century which made possible the awarding of meaningful cash prizes to deserving artists and fellowships to worthy students. The early precedent set in those years has now snowballed to the point that there are thirty-seven exhibition prizes awarded to artists and fifteen prizes to students, annually. In addition the Henry Ward Ranger Fund has purchased and distributed to public collections of the country over 400 paintings by living artists since 1919, and the Edwin Austin Abbey Mural Fund has commissioned ten major paintings throughout the country—such as the panels in the Eisenhower Museum, Abilene, Kansas, by Louis Bouché and Ross Moffett, the Harry S. Truman Library murals by Thomas Hart Benton and the murals in the Indiana State Capitol by Leon Kroll.

The security of the National Academy's public image as represented, among other evidences, by the prize endowments was strangely set against a concurrent series of events which seemed to want to destroy that image of success and authority. In the final weeks of the Nineteenth Century the Academy found itself again without a permanent home of its own.

With the school located in "temporary" quarters at 109th Street and Amsterdam Avenue—for the succeeding forty years, as it turned out—and the exhibition program being held in rented quarters at the American Fine Arts Society on Fifty-Seventh Street, the Academy's public image began to fragment. Contributing to this situation were a fire in the school building in 1905 which destroyed some school records, casts and works of art; the exhibition of "Eight American Painters" at the Macbeth Gallery in 1908 which was aimed directly at the authority of the Academy; the first exhibition of the Independents in 1910; and ultimately the real H-bomb of its time, the Armory Show of 1913 which introduced the European developments of Cubism, Fauvism and Expressionism to America.

The changes wrought by the events surrounding World War I affected the Academy just as they did the rest of the country. Buffeted by the agonies of political and aesthetic battles of the Twentieth Century, the Academy thrived to the point of finally being able to house all of its activities under its own roof again. This was accomplished through the generosity of Archer M. Huntington who bequeathed his Fifth Avenue townhouse to the Academy in 1940. Again a national crisis coincided with a comparable crisis and its solution at the National Academy. Out of the turmoil of World War II and its cultural-political upheavals the Academy found itself with a unified home for only the second time in its history. The present headquarters on upper Fifth Avenue provide the most spacious and suitable home the Academy has known.

The world of art today is no longer the even moderately homogeneous vocation which it seemed to be a hundred years ago. Gone is the ancient tradition of master-student continuance of craft and expertise. Today the means of producing visual images have multiplied astronomically and combined with the disparate aesthetic, cultural and geographical influences to produce possibilities for artists hardly dreamed of even by such a worthy dreamer as Thomas Cole. In spite of this splintered world there is still that deep seated need among artists of this country for a home, a focus, a place organized for and by them.

This 150th Anniversary Exhibition, which illuminates the place that the National Academy of Design has occupied in our national art world, points to the future of the Academy as the center for all well-established artists of every aesthetic persuasion.

GEORGE NORTH MORRIS

150th Anniversary Gold Medal

The President and the Council of the National Academy of Design commissioned Donald De Lue, NA to design this medal to commemorate the contribution the Academy has made to the fine arts during the 150 years since its founding: in providing training for students in painting, sculpture and the graphic arts; in exhibiting the works of professional artists; and as a trustee of many and varied funds for the benefit of the public, the professional artist, and the student.

The beautiful design for the medal has its basis in mythology. On the obverse side is Pegasus in flight above the clouds reaching for the stars. Prometheus is depicted on the reverse side making his gift to mankind.

The medal was awarded by the Jury of Awards in the 150th Annual Exhibition (February, 1975) for professional merit in the four exhibiting classes as follows:

Oil—RICHARD WYNN
Sculpture—C. PAUL JENNEWEIN NA
Graphic Arts—JOHN FENTON
Watercolor—DONG KINGMAN NA

It is also being given to the following patrons in deep appreciation of their financial support of the retrospective exhibition, "A Century and a Half of American Art":

Max Abramovitz NA	Alfred Easton Poor PNA
Alice K. Bache	Paul Thiry NA
C.B.S. Foundation	Dagmar H. Tribble
Lucille Cohen	Lila Acheson Wallace
Wallace K. Harrison NA	Chi-Chuan Wang
John Koch NA	Catharine Morris Wright NA

Above: Obverse.   *Below:* Reverse.

The following abbreviations are used in the biographical entries:

NA – National Academician
ANA – Associate of the National Academy
HM(P) – Honorary Member (professional)
PNA – President National Academy

Dimensions are in inches; height precedes width.
Paintings are in oil unless otherwise indicated.

We acknowledge the assistance of the Frick Art Reference Library in furnishing many of the photographs of the paintings from the collection of the National Academy of Design reproduced herein.

Painting

EDWIN AUSTIN ABBEY (1852–1911)
(ANA 1901, NA 1902)
Coronation of King Edward VII (c. 1901)
27 × 44 inches.
National Academy of Design.
Gift of Mrs. Abbey.

Abbey was born in Philadelphia and studied at the Pennsylvania Academy under Christian Schussele. His primary interest in art was illustration, and his natural antiquarianism led him to a fascination with the English 17th and 18th centuries. At the age of nineteen he joined the staff of *Harper's Weekly* in New York. In 1878 he embarked for England to become a more-or-less permanent expatriate. Abbey's sense of drama and pageantry soon began to assert itself. The illustration of plays such as Goldsmith's "She Stoops to Conquer" and Shakespeare's comedies followed. Gradually painting replaced illustration and for the last quarter century of his life mural painting provided Abbey with the dramatic scope he had long sought. His panels of the Arthurian legend in the Boston Public Library and historical murals in the Pennsylvania State Capitol, Harrisburg are his two principal American commissions. King Edward VII commissioned him to paint the official coronation portrait and a mural of the coronation, for which the present painting is a study. Exhibited NAD 1874–5, 1906.

FREDERICK S. AGATE (1803–1844)
(Founder NA 1826)
The Dead Child. 30 × 37 inches. Signed, 1827.
National Academy of Design. Gift of artist's great grandniece, 1940.

Agate, born of English immigrant parents at Sparta, Westchester County, New York, went to New York City at the age of fifteen to study drawing under John Rubens Smith. Seven years later he and schoolmate Thomas S. Cummings left Smith to study with Samuel F. B. Morse at the American Academy. Agate and Cummings were the two students who were prevented from drawing independently at the old Academy and who instigated the art rebellion resulting in the formation of the National Academy of Design. Cummings later became treasurer and historian of the early years of the Academy. Agate established himself as a historical and portrait painter at a studio at 152 Broadway. A prolific artist, he exhibited ten or fifteen paintings annually at the Academy. He traveled for two years, 1834–36, in Europe, and returned to the United States in declining health. He was, however, able to produce his semi-religious, moralistic work until shortly before his death.
Exhibited NAD 1826–34, 1837–44.

Frederick S. Agate, NA
The Dead Child. Oil
National Academy of Design

John W. Alexander, NA
Portrait of Thurlow Weed. Oil
National Academy of Design

JOHN W. ALEXANDER (1856–1915)
(ANA 1901, NA 1902, PNA 1909–15)
Portrait of Thurlow Weed (c. 1880). 50 × 40 inches.
Signed.
National Academy of Design.
Gift of Mrs. J. W. Alexander, 1942.

Alexander was born in Allegheny, Pennsylvania, became a telegraph messenger boy, and found his way into art through his early discovered ability to illustrate. The 1877 strike in Pittsburgh provided him with the kind of drama which he used as illustrator for *Harper's Weekly*. He went to Germany to study painting and paid his way by sending home drawings to *Harper's*. By the mid-1880's he was traveling back and forth from this country to Europe to draw the heads of famous Europeans for both *Harper's Weekly* and *Century Magazine*. In 1901 he settled in New York permanently and concentrated on portrait painting. The last fourteen years of his life saw the production of an avalanche of work: portraits of scores of the day's most prominent people, mural commissions (one of which, in the Carnegie Institute, Pittsburgh, is still one of the largest ever painted by an American), and endless hours of support for art organizations. In addition to the Presidency of the National Academy of Design he was also President of the National Institute of Arts and Letters, the School Art League (a special enthusiasm), and the MacDowell Club. He was a member of many other societies and won numerous awards for his genial, brisk, and sometimes characterful painting.
Exhibited NAD 1882–84, 1886, 1895, 1902, 1904–05, 1907–12, 1914–15.

THOMAS P. ANSHUTZ (1851–1912) (ANA 1910)
Figure Piece (c. 1910). 40 × 36 inches. Signed.
National Academy of Design.

Anshutz, a native of Newport, Kentucky, arrived in New York in 1873 to study art at the National Academy under L. E. Wilmarth. Two years later he continued his studies at the Pennsylvania Academy under Eakins and Schussele. In 1881 he became a member of the faculty of that school. A year's sabbatical in 1885 for study in Paris under Doucet and Bouguereau at the Académie Julian was followed by a return to the Pennsylvania Academy's staff, where he remained for the rest of his life. He was evidently a superb teacher if one can judge by his students: Henri, Luks, Sloan, Redfield, Glackens, and Garber, among others. Anshutz was a solid painter who prepared each major canvas with many studies. He received numerous honors and succeeded William M. Chase in 1909 as head of the faculty of the Pennsylvania Academy.
Exhibited NAD 1880, 1884, 1908, 1910, 1912.

Thomas P. Anshutz, ANA
Figure Piece. Oil
National Academy of Design

John James Audubon, HM(P)
Study of Birds, Black Grouse or Heath Grouse. Oil
National Academy of Design

JOHN JAMES AUDUBON (1785–1851)
(H.M. (P) 1833)
Study of Birds, Black Grouse or Heath Grouse
(c. 1833). 25 × 30 inches.
National Academy of Design.

Audubon was born of a French sea captain father and Creole mother in Santo Domingo. He returned to France with his father to receive a good bourgeois education. Part of his schooling was the interest in nature disseminated by Rousseau and Lamarck, and Audubon responded by doing drawings of French birds. Having made the decision to study art, he became a drawing pupil of the official artist of the Revolution, Jacques Louis David, for a few months before leaving for the United States in 1803. He later began his career as artist-naturalist when he entered into partnership with Ferdinand Rozier in a succession of losing business ventures in Kentucky. There he met Daniel Boone and, more importantly, Alexander Wilson, America's first ornithologist. The two naturalists did not get along, and it may be that this antagonism spurred Audubon in his own work. He drew and painted studies of birds wherever he went—down the Mississippi, Louisiana, Florida, Labrador—paying his way with portraits. He had by this time devised a plan for a book of engraved reproductions of his paintings and found Robert Havell, Jr., in London, who became his chief engraver. The present painting was done during one of the artist's brief stays in this country, 1831–1834. Audubon's reputation rests primarily on his three major books, *Birds of America*, *Ornithological Biographies* and *Quadrupeds of America*, but his original watercolors and oil paintings are superb works of art.
Exhibited NAD 1833.

GEORGE AUGUSTUS BAKER, JR. (1821–1880)
(ANA 1846, NA 1851)
Self Portrait. 30 × 25 inches. Exhibited 1847.
National Academy of Design.

Baker was the son of a miniaturist of the same name who was born in France and settled in New York. Following his father's lead he started out as a painter of miniatures on ivory and became an instant success. His first year he produced 150 miniatures at $5 apiece. He supported himself this way for the next seven years while studying portrait painting at the National Academy of Design. From 1844–46 he studied in Europe. After his return to New York he promptly became established as a painter of oil portraits, especially of women and children. A portrait of a child by Baker was exhibited in the Paris Exposition of 1867. The last fourteen years of his life he lived in Darien, Connecticut, where he carried on his successful portrait career.
Exhibited NAD 1838, 1840–44, 1846–72, 1874–79.

GIFFORD BEAL (1879–1956)
(ANA 1908, NA 1914)
The Mall, Central Park. 30 × 40 inches.
Signed, Gifford Beal 1913.
National Academy of Design.
Diploma painting, acquired 1915.

Beal was born in New York, graduated from Princeton in 1900, and studied art under William Merritt Chase for ten years. He also worked with George Bridgman and Frank Vincent DuMond at the Art Students' League. Beal's specialties were marine and figure painting while his depictions of the circus are among the best of this genre. He also did considerable mural painting, some of which were executed in egg tempera. He was commissioned by the Council of the National Academy, trustees of the Edwin Austin Abbey Mural Fund, to paint seven panels portraying the life of scientist John Henry at his alma mater. He also painted a mural in the Department of the Interior building, Washington, D.C. Beal was president of the Art Students' League, 1914–1929. He received eighteen major art awards and is represented in more than twenty-five museums. He was a member of the American Academy of Arts and Letters, and he was honored with a memorial exhibition by that organization in 1957.
Exhibited NAD 1901–21, 1923, 1930–39, 1942–43, 1945–52, 1954–56.

CECILIA BEAUX (1855–1942)
(ANA 1894, NA 1902)
Portrait of Cecil (Cecil Kent Drinker) (1891).
64 × 34½ inches. Signed, Cecilia Beaux.
Philadelphia Museum of Art.

Beaux was born in Philadelphia and raised by her aunt and grandmother. Her Quaker uncle, William Biddle, provided the money for her subsequent education. At first this consisted of drawing in a private studio and looking at the paintings in the Pennsylvania Academy and Philadelphia's Gibson Collection. Uncle Will refused to let her study with Eakins at the Academy on moral grounds ("rabble of untidy art students", etc.). She began to teach private pupils and instructed at a private school to prove to her family that she was serious about her art. A portrait by Beaux was hung in the Pennsylvania Academy in 1885 and in the Paris Salon the following year. This success convinced her to go to Paris where she studied under six different teachers at the Académie Julian from 1888 to 1890. Ten succeeding years back in Philadelphia were followed in 1900 by Beaux's moving to New York. Her fluent style brought numerous portrait commissions and awards from art societies, including the Gold Medal from the American Academy of Arts and Letters, but her mature work never progressed beyond her early plateau of excellence.
Exhibited NAD 1892–97, 1899, 1906, 1908–09, 1911–15, 1917, 1927, 1930, 1934, 1939.

George Bellows, NA
The White Horse. Oil
Worcester Art Museum, Worcester, Massachusetts

GEORGE BELLOWS (1882–1925)
(ANA 1909, NA 1913)
The White Horse. 34⅛ × 44⅛ inches.
Signed, Geo. Bellows.
Worcester Art Museum, Worcester,
Massachusetts.

Bellows, a native of Columbus, Ohio, graduated
from Ohio State University in 1903 and arrived
in New York the following year to study under
Robert Henri, Kenneth Hayes Miller, and H. G.
Maratta. He became fascinated by the energy and
color of the Big City and put these characteristics
into his painting. His affinity for Goya and Dau-
mier is apparent in his early work, such as "Forty-
Two Kids" (1907) and "Sharkey's" (1909). By
this latter year his work had so impressed his contemporaries that he became the youngest artist
ever to become an Associate of the National Academy. He taught at the Art Students' League in
1910 and in 1918–1919. He also taught at The Art
Institute of Chicago in 1919. Bellows's experience
with the Maratta color system and later with Jay
Hambidge's "Dynamic Symmetry" seduced him
into introducing an artificial sort of "knowledge"
into his painting which contributed to a weaken-
ing of the artist's impact. However, whenever he
painted without that self-consciousness, as in his
portraits and landscapes, he maintained his ability to communicate strongly in paint. In his later
years he turned to lithography and illustration as
additional outlets for his talent. He continuously
won prizes at major exhibitions, and his work can
be found in the principal American museums.
Exhibited NAD 1907–18.

FRANK W. BENSON (1862–1951)
(ANA 1897, NA 1905)
Girl in a Red Shawl. 32¼ × 32¼ inches.
Signed, Frank W. Benson, 1890.
Museum of Fine Arts, Boston.

Benson, born in Salem, Massachusetts, studied at
the Boston Museum of Fine Arts and at the Académie Julian, Paris, for a total of five years. After
his return to Boston he established a reputation as
a painter of society figures. Appointed an in-
structor at the Museum School, he began to win
Prizes, first at the National Academy (Clarke
Prize, 1891), then in Paris, Chicago (Potter Palmer
Prize and Medal, 1910), and other centers. In 1912
he started to etch, principally plates of wild fowl.
After they were first exhibited in 1915, his reputation as an etcher began to overtake that of a
painter. More prizes, this time for his etchings,
followed. Benson was a member of the American
Academy of Arts and Letters. One of his largest
works was a set of seven mural panels in the Library of Congress.
Exhibited NAD 1886, 1888–96, 1898, 1904–06,
1908, 1921–22, 1925–26, 1930–33, 1935–36, 1939–
42, 1946, 1952.

Frank W. Benson, NA
Girl in a Red Shawl. Oil
Museum of Fine Arts, Boston

EUGÈNE BERMAN (1899–1972)
(ANA 1950, NA 1954)
Greek Temple at Sunset (1962). 42 × 30 inches.
Sylvia Marlowe, Courtesy, Larcada Gallery,
New York.

Berman was born in St. Petersburg, Russia, and
fled with his family to Paris after the Bolshevik
revolution. Berman studied art in Paris and held
his first show in 1925 with his brother, Leonid,
and other congenial artists who professed a similar
sort of Neo-Romanticism. Scorned by artists
more structurally minded, he was branded as a
reactionary. Berman traveled to Italy where he
could study fantastic ruins at first hand. There he
met and explored with Chirico the problems of
space and time which interested both artists. In
1935 he came to New York. Here he began to
design for the theater, first in Connecticut, then
New York, and back to Paris as his reputation as
a designer for opera spread. The Metropolitan
Opera, in particular, commissioned him to design
sets for "Rigoletto", "La Forza del Destino",
"The Barber of Seville", and "Don Giovanni".
In 1957 Berman retired to Rome where he continued to paint his personal interpretations of
ancient buildings and landscapes.
Exhibited NAD 1949–50, 1969, 1973.

ALBERT BIERSTADT (1830–1902)
(HM(P) 1858, NA 1860)
Yosemite Valley. 54 × 84 inches.
Signed, A. Bierstadt.
Mrs. Jesse C. Reese, Jr., New York.

Bierstadt, born near Düsseldorf, Germany, educated in his immigrant home, New Bedford,
Massachusetts, decided to be an artist in his early
twenties. He returned to Düsseldorf for four years
of training under Achenbach and Lessing, then to
Rome for additional study. Back in the United
States in 1857, he joined an expedition setting out
to survey a Western wagon route. This trip
awakened in him a sense of the pictorial possibilities of Western grandeur which became his chief
subject matter. From 1861 on he turned out a succession of grandiose views of Rocky Mountain
scenery which found a ready market in the "Mani-
fest Destiny" minded East. Bierstadt made three
trips to Europe, where he was deluged with
medals and other distinctions. In his late years he
included animals in his repertoire of subjects. By
then his fashion had passed as subsequent generations saw his work as somewhat artificial decoration.
Exhibited NAD 1858–65, 1867–68, 1871–72, 1874–
77, 1880–81, 1884–88.

Robert F. Blum, NA
Two Idlers. Oil
National Academy of Design

ROBERT F. BLUM (1857–1903)
(ANA 1888, NA 1893)
Two Idlers. 29 × 40 inches. Signed, 1888–89.
National Academy of Design.

Blum, born of German immigrant parents in Cincinnati, dropped out of high school to work in a lithographic plant. In 1875 he entered the McMicken School of Design and there met schoolmates Alfred Brennan and Kenyon Cox. He developed an early interest in Japanese art through fans and boxes and through a visit to the Japanese Pavilion at the Philadelphia Centennial Exhibition. He remained in Philadelphia with Cox to study at the Pennsylvania Academy the winter of 1876–77. Blum then went to New York and found a patron for his brisk drawings in A. W. Drake, art editor of *Scribner's Monthly* and *St. Nicholas Magazine.* A trip to Europe with Drake in 1879 enabled him not only to become acquainted with the great art of the past but to meet artists of the present, too, notably Whistler and fellow townsman Duveneck who were sharing a studio in Venice. Back in New York he did theatrical illustrations for Drake's magazines and began to paint wall decorations in private residences of the city. Much travel followed, punctuated with annual jaunts to Europe through the Eighties. In 1889 he finally was able to visit Japan and to execute drawings to illustrate books and articles. He stayed there two years and found inspiration for his most important painting, "The Candy Blower", shown at the National Academy in 1892 and now in the Metropolitan Museum, New York. The Cincinnati Art Museum possesses the largest collection of Blum's work.
Exhibited NAD 1881–82, 1884, 1888–90, 1893, 1897.

LOUIS BOUCHÉ (1896–1969)
(ANA 1948, NA 1950)
The Subway. 20 × 24 inches. Signed,
Louis Bouché, 1942.
National Academy of Design.
Diploma painting, 1950.

Bouché was born in New York and, after public schooling, studied under Frank V. DuMond at the Art Students' League and under J. P. Laurens in Paris. After returning to New York he embarked on a highly successful career, painting the world around him in a fresh, breezy manner. Nothing seemed too trivial or too grand for his approach. In 1933 Bouché was awarded a Guggenheim Fellowship. For many years he taught at the Art Students' League and maintained a studio on West Tenth Street. During his career he painted murals in Radio City Music Hall, the Attorney General's office in the Justice Department building, Washington, D. C., in the Interior Department building, Washington, and in the Eisenhower Foundation building, Abilene, Kansas. In 1959 Bouché was elected vice president of the National Institute of Arts and Letters. In 1962 he won the Benjamin Altman Prize. His work can be found in the Metropolitan Museum, the Whitney Museum, the American Academy of Arts and Letters, and other leading collections, public and private.
Exhibited NAD 1944–45, 1947–70.

Louis Bouché, NA
The Subway. Oil
National Academy of Design

DEWITT C. BOUTELLE (1820–1884)
(ANA 1852)
Catskill Grandeur, Artist Painting. 52½ × 47 inches.
Signed, DeWitt Clinton Boutelle, 1870.
Mr. and Mrs. George J. Arden, New York.

Boutelle was born in Troy, New York, named
for the illustrious governor of the state, and early
developed a feeling for the Hudson River Valley
by drawing the local landscape independently as
a teenager. By 1846 he had progressed far enough
to locate briefly in New York City. In 1848 he
moved across the river to Baskingridge, New
Jersey, for three years and tried New York again
from 1851 to 1855. Boutelle worked in Philadelphia for a few years, but from 1858 until his death
lived and painted in Bethlehem, Pennsylvania.
Beside the National Academy he exhibited at
the Pennsylvania Academy, the Boston Athenaeum, the Washington Art Association, and the
American Art-Union.
Exhibited NAD 1846, 1850–53, 1855, 1857, 1859,
1865, 1871, 1874.

JOHN G. BROWN (1831–1913)
(ANA 1861, NA 1863)
Resting in the Woods (Girl under a Tree).
18⅜ × 12⅛ inches. Signed, J. G. Brown, 1866.
Jo Ann and Julian Ganz, Jr., Los Angeles.

Brown was born into a poor family in Durham,
England. During a seven year apprenticeship to a
glass cutter in Newcastle-on-Tyne he studied art
with Scott Lowdes. Later he worked with William
D. Scott in Scotland. At the age of twenty-two he
went to London and earned his living drawing
and painting portraits. Brown emigrated to the
United States as the direct result of hearing a music
hall entertainer sing a song about the fascinations
of American life. In Brooklyn he supported himself with his glass cutting trade. His drawings for
stained glass designs so impressed his employer,
William Owen, that the latter helped him to study
in New York with Thomas S. Cummings. In
1856 Brown married Owen's daughter, Mary.
He rented a studio in the Old Studio Building at
51 West Tenth Street, New York, in 1860 and
started painting street children in the neighbor-
hood for which he received $5 to $30 each. "His
First Cigar" was exhibited at the National Academy that year and gained him national promi-
nence. Brown's career was founded on his depiction of such genre subjects as the poor people
around him. It is ironic that his undoubtedly
honest sentimentality about the poor earned him
an annual income of forty to fifty thousand
dollars.
Exhibited NAD 1858–90.

John G. Brown, NA
Resting in the Woods (*Girl Under a Tree*). Oil
Jo Ann and Julian Ganz, Jr., Los Angeles

George DeForest Brush, NA
The Escape. Oil
Philadelphia Museum of Art

GEORGE DEFOREST BRUSH (1855–1941)
(ANA 1888, NA 1908)
The Escape. 15½ × 19½ inches.
Signed, Geo. DeForest Brush, 1882.
Philadelphia Museum of Art.

Brush, raised in Danbury, Connecticut, began studying art at the age of sixteen at the National Academy under L. E. Wilmarth. Three years later he enrolled in the École des Beaux-Arts, Paris, where, with J. Alden Weir and Abbott Thayer, he became a pupil of J. L. Gérôme. The "French polish" agreed with Brush's temperament. After returning to the United States in 1880, he traveled to Wyoming and Montana with his brother for several years. The paintings which resulted from his experience were idealized depictions of Indian life in the approved Salon manner, a far cry from Catlin's earlier vigor. Such paintings had limited sale after Brush's return to New York in 1885, and he maintained himself and his new wife and children by teaching at the Art Students' League. He began painting mother-and-child themes, and these finally brought him rewards which allowed him and his family to travel to Europe several times and to buy a farm in Dublin, New Hampshire. He won the First Hallgarten Prize at the National Academy in 1888, gold medals at the Pan-American and Louisiana Purchase Expositions, and a Yale University honorary degree. He was a member of the American Academy of Arts and Letters.
Exhibited NAD 1875, 1877, 1882, 1886, 1888–90.

EMIL CARLSEN (1853–1932)
(ANA 1904, NA 1906)
The Wild Swan. 48¾ × 58½ inches. Signed,
Emil Carlsen, 1902.
National Academy of Design.
Diploma painting, 1906.

Carlsen was born in Copenhagen, Denmark, and studied architecture prior to his emigration to the United States at the age of nineteen. There had been several marine painters in his family, so he also picked up the habit of painting the sea, a life-long interest. In this country he first worked as an architectural draughtsman. He shortly abandoned this career and returned to Europe to study the old masters of painting, particularly Chardin. The reigning Impressionists had little effect on his style. Carlsen preferred a static, flat patterned world with few surface interruptions. He later turned to religious painting and called his version of Christ walking on the water, "Oh Ye of Little Faith", the expression of his personal creed.
Exhibited NAD 1885–87, 1894–95, 1903, 1905–21, 1923–32.

Emil Carlsen, NA
The Wild Swan. Oil
National Academy of Design

William Merritt Chase, NA
Tenth Street Studio. Oil
Mr. and Mrs. George J. Arden, New York

WILLIAM MERRITT CHASE (1849–1916)
(ANA 1888, NA 1890)
Tenth Street Studio. 18 × 20 inches.
Mr. and Mrs. George J. Arden, New York.

Chase, a native of Indiana, first studied art at the National Academy under J. O. Eaton. A syndicate of four interested men sent him to Munich in 1872 to learn the then popular bravura brush technique for which that city's artists were famous. Hard work and several medals won at the Munich Royal Academy combined to earn him early fame. He returned to New York in 1878 with a large collection of decorative arts and pictures and set up a studio at 51 West Tenth Street which was a model for all artists' studios of the time: ornate, luxurious, crowded, and with a steady north light. He taught at the newly organized Art Students' League and became President of the Society of American Artists. He was a large, genial man who socialized well, attracted vast numbers of students to his classes, and became a major influence in American art. Chase's school at Southampton, Long Island, during the '90s was one of the first successful enterprises of its sort. It established the format for many succeeding similar ventures, notably that of Charles Hawthorne, a student of Chase, in Provincetown. Examples of his work are in most of the leading museums of the United States.
Exhibited NAD 1871, 1875, 1877–79, 1888–95, 1897–99, 1902–08, 1910–16.

FREDERIC E. CHURCH (1826–1900)
(ANA 1848, NA 1849)
Scene on the Magdalene. 28 × 42 inches.
Exhibited 1855.
National Academy of Design.

Church was born in Hartford, Connecticut, and received his first art instruction from Benjamin A. Coe and A. H. Emmons. His real master was Thomas Cole, with whom he lived and painted in Catskill, New York, from 1844 to 1848. The Hudson Valley could not hold his vision or ambitions. First, Church visited Niagara Falls, then the northern coast of Labrador to paint icebergs. From there he went to the tropics and Andes in South America in 1853 and in 1857. In Ecuador and Colombia he found his most congenial, super-romantic subjects, an amalgam of vision and fact. After 1877 his advancing rheumatism forced him to give up painting during the last twenty years of his life, which he spent in his oriental palace on the Hudson. Church's romanticism encompassed not only far away places but also remote times, such as his paintings of the Aegean area which included views of the Athenian Acropolis. His large, rich canvases can be found in major American museums.
Exhibited NAD 1845–57, 1859, 1861, 1863, 1865–70, 1872, 1874, 1876, 1878.

THOMAS COLE (1801–1848) (Founder NA 1826)
Mill Dam on the Catskill Creek (1841).
22 × 30 inches. Signed, T. Cole (or T.C. 1841).
Henry M. Fuller, New York.

Cole was born in Lancashire, England, into the Wordsworthian period of romantic travel. His voracious reading habits introduced him and his family to possibilities available in America and they arrived in Philadelphia in 1819. Thomas went to work as an engraver and stayed in the city when his family moved to Steubenville, Ohio. He shipped with a friend to the West Indies and back, then traveled on foot from Philadelphia to Ohio. Further shaky business ventures by his father brought Cole to Philadelphia again, this time to study art at the Pennsylvania Academy. Later he moved to New York and painted in his father's house on Greenwich Street to which the family had moved in the interim. Paintings exhibited in a shop caught the attention of Trumbull and Durand, who bought his canvases. His reputation as a painter of the Palisades and other Hudson River views spread rapidly, William Cullen Bryant becoming one of his chief publicists. Cole took part in the formation of the National Academy of Design and was the main discoverer of the beauties of the Catskill Mountains. He continued to travel, to England (where he met Lawrence and Turner and exhibited at the Royal Academy) and to France and Italy (1831–32). Back in New York he worked on a series of five canvases on a single allegorical theme, "Course of Empire," a commission from Luman Reed. Cole then settled in Catskill, New York and painted more allegories ("Voyage of Life") as well as landscapes. Back in Catskill he died while working on yet another allegory.
Exhibited NAD 1826–38, 1840–48.

JOHN E. COSTIGAN (1888–1972)
(ANA 1924, NA 1928)
The Sun's Reflections. 45 × 45 inches. Signed,
J. E. Costigan.
National Academy of Design.
Exhibited 1925. Diploma painting, acquired 1928.

Costigan was a native of Providence, Rhode Island, a first cousin of George M. Cohan. Orphaned as a child, he was brought by Cohan's parents to New York at the age of fifteen where they found him a job with a lithography company producing theatrical posters. Here he observed the print process in action, a skill later used in his etchings. He was largely self-taught though he underwent a few weeks of instruction at the Art Students' League. For several years he drew from the model at the Kit Kat Club, an informal sketch group patronized by leading illustrators and commercial artists. Costigan served as a private in the Infantry in the First World War, and in the years following he began to win prizes at major exhibitions. During the 1930's he did magazine illustration to survive the Depression, and the Second World War found him in a war plant as a machine operator. He refused to paint portraits because "the subjects want flattering pictures." Costigan's work can be seen at the Metropolitan Museum, The Art Institute of Chicago, the Library of Congress, and other leading institutions.
Exhibited NAD 1917–69, 1973.

Jasper F. Cropsey, NA
The Quiet Valley, Hudson River. Oil
Mr. and Mrs. George J. Arden, New York

JASPER F. CROPSEY (1823–1900)
(ANA 1844, NA 1851)
The Quiet Valley, Hudson River. 32 × 49 inches.
Signed, J. F. Cropsey 1846 (the "4" has been
slightly obscured and is not certain).
Mr. and Mrs. George J. Arden, New York.

Cropsey was born and raised in the vicinity of
the Hudson River and it was inevitable that he
would become a painter of the Valley. He started
to be an architect but a failure in that field turned
him to landscape painting. He taught himself by
expanding romantic architectural renderings into
imaginary landscapes. He found that the visions of
Thomas Cole provided an empathic example and
when he went to study in Italy, 1847–49, he even
used Cole's old Roman studio. Cropsey's work
of the first half of the 'Fifties was closely similar to
the imagery and technique of Cole. During these
years he made a pilgrimage to discover other picturesque glories of the Northeast, New Hampshire's White Mountains, Rhode Island's shore,
and upstate New York, especially Niagara Falls.
He also discovered the art of Frederic E. Church.
From 1856 to 1863 Cropsey lived in London and
the painting influence of Church replaced Cole's.
He painted "Autumn on the Hudson" in 1860,
spurred by having seen Church's "Heart of the
Andes," to show that the grandeur of the Hudson
Valley was equal to that of South America. The
five by nine foot canvas was bought and presented
to Queen Victoria. Upon his return to America in
1863 because of the Civil War, his success was
repeated here.
Exhibited NAD 1843–47, 1850–60, 1863–99.

JOHN STEUART CURRY (1897–1946)
(ANA 1937, NA 1943)
Belgian Stallions. 30 × 25½ inches.
Signed, John Steuart Curry, 1938.
National Academy of Design.

Curry was born into a farming family in the rural
community of Dunavant, Kansas. Youthful interest in drawing led to the Kansas City Art Institute
and then to The Art Institute of Chicago. Curry
then worked as an assistant to illustrator Harvey
Dunn in Tenafly, New Jersey, and began to do
illustrations for *The Saturday Evening Post* and *St.
Nicholas Magazine.* Never really interested in illustration, he went to Paris in 1926 to study. He
returned to continue studying at the Art Students'
League in 1927, learning the craft of lithography.
"Baptism in Kansas," painted the following year,
was heralded as "the work of a new master of
American genre" and was bought by Gertrude
Vanderbilt Whitney. He received prizes (Carnegie International, 1933), purchases (Metropolitan Museum), and critical acclaim. A circus series
done while traveling with Ringling Brothers in
1932 was particularly well received. The late
'Thirties saw Curry develop into one of the better
muralists in that period. His panels for the Kansas
State Capitol in Topeka he considered to be his
principal achievement. He was the original Artist-
in-Residence at an American college, in his case,
the University of Wisconsin.
Exhibited NAD 1924, 1931–32, 1935–41, 1943–44,
1946.

Charles T. Dix, ANA
Marblehead Rocks. Oil
National Academy of Design

THOMAS W. DEWING (1851–1938)
(ANA 1887, NA 1888)
The Sorcerer's Slave. 18 × 9½ inches. Signed, 1877.
National Academy of Design.

Dewing was born in Boston, worked briefly as a
lithographer, studied for three years in Paris under
J. J. Lefebvre, and, in 1879, returned to live in New
York for the rest of his life. The present painting
was done during his Paris studies. Dewing's characteristic painting style was the depiction on small
canvases of languid, meditating women who seem
to inhabit an ideal world hardly disturbed by the
movement of air. He also did portraits of men,
women, and children as well as mural compositions for architect Stanford White who designed
some of his frames. Dewing was a member of
the Society of American Artists and taught at
the Art Students' League. He joined the group
"Ten American Painters" along with Weir,
Twachtman, Benson, and Metcalf. He was
elected to the National Institute of Arts and Letters
in 1908 and did little painting after 1920. The
Freer Gallery and the Gellatly Collection, both
part of the Smithsonian Institution, Washington,
D.C., contain the largest concentration of his
work.
Exhibited NAD 1879–80, 1887–92, 1895–96, 1930.

CHARLES T. DIX (1838–1873) (ANA 1861)
Marblehead Rocks. 38 × 60½ inches. Signed.
National Academy of Design.
Gift of Mr. W. F. Havemeyer, 1911.

Dix was born in Albany, New York, the son of
General John A. Dix. He graduated from Union
College at the age of eighteen and studied painting in New York until the outbreak of the Civil
War. He was an officer for the duration of the
war, and immediately afterwards sailed to Europe
for further study. Dix's career was cut short at the
relatively early age of thirty-three while working
in Rome. He exhibited at the Royal Academy,
London, during his European stay.
Exhibited NAD 1861, 1870–72.

Guy Pène Du Bois, NA
Morning, Paris Cafe. Oil
Whitney Museum of American Art, New York

GUY PÈNE DU BOIS (1844–1958)
(ANA 1937, NA 1940)
Morning, Paris Café. 36¼ × 28¾ inches.
Signed, Guy Pène du Bois/26.
Whitney Museum of American Art, New York.

Du Bois, born in Brooklyn, was a member of a French family tracing its roots back to New Orleans in 1738. A high school dropout, he became the youngest student in Chase's school in 1899. During the following six years he studied with DuMond, K. H. Miller, Beckwith, and Henri. In 1905 he was in Paris getting his first taste of life on the Left Bank. He started reporting for the *New York American*, the newspaper where his father had been music critic. He stayed at *The American* for seven years and then transferred to *The Tribune* as an assistant to art critic, Royal Cortissoz. Further experience as editor and critic sharpened his verbal skills at the same time he was sharpening his visual ability with irony and wit. Six years in France in the late 'Twenties was a turning point in his career as a painter. His earlier work was related to the New York Realists, reflecting their interest in the vigor of city life. The French period clarified his color and broadened his outlook. Though Du Bois was mainly a satirical genre painter, he also painted large wall decorations and postoffice murals. Numerous prizes came his way (Los Angeles Museum, 1928; The Art Institute of Chicago, 1930; 2nd Altman Prize, National Academy, 1936; Corcoran Silver Medal, 1937; 1st Altman Prize, NAD, 1945; and Salmagundi Club, 1946), and his paintings have been acquired by leading American museums.
Exhibited NAD 1927, 1932, 1935–40, 1942, 1944–45, 1947, 1949–52, 1959.

PETER PAUL DUGGAN (1810–1861)
(ANA 1849, NA 1851)
Lazzar House in the West Indies.
18 × 24½ inches. Exhibited NAD 1849. Signed.
National Academy of Design. Diploma painting, acquired 1852.

Duggan was born in Ireland and brought to the United States as a child in 1810. Mostly self-taught, he became well known in New York between 1844 and 1856 as a painter of portraits in crayon and as a designer of medals for the American Art-Union. Duggan was a roamer who visited the West Indies during his years in America, but ill health forced him to give up an active life. He spent his last five years in London and then Paris, where he died.
Exhibited NAD 1844–45, 1847–51, 1855–56, 1862.

Frank Vincent DuMond, NA
Christ and the Fishermen. Oil
Mrs. Walter M. Perry, Darien, Connecticut

Asher B. Durand, PNA
Morning of Life. Oil
National Academy of Design

Asher B. Durand, PNA
Evening of Life. Oil
National Academy of Design

FRANK VINCENT DUMOND (1865–1951)
(ANA 1900, NA 1906)
Christ and the Fishermen. 52 × 64 inches.
Signed, F. V. Du Mond, 1891.
Mrs. Walter M. Perry, Darien, Connecticut.

DuMond was a native of Rochester, New York, who came to New York as a young man to study at the Art Students' League in 1884 for a year. He then went to Paris for a year's instruction under Boulanger, Lefebvre, and Constant at Julian's Academy. For six years DuMond worked first for the New York *Daily Graphic* and *Harper's Weekly* as a newspaper artist. His assignment to draw the funeral of Samuel J. Tilden in Yonkers proved to be a coup. The drawing's reproduction in *Harper's* so impressed editor Horace Bradley that when he became president of the Art Students' League, he hired DuMond to teach there. It was the beginning of a fifty-nine year career of teaching at the League and through his classes passed some of America's most prominent artists. His own painting is seen rather less than that of his students, but it can be found in the San Francisco Public Library, the Hotel des Artistes, New York, and in the museums of Portland, Oregon, and Denver. His work won medals at the Paris Salon of 1890, the Pan-American Exposition in Buffalo, 1901, and in the St. Louis Exposition, 1904. He was a member of the National Institute of Arts and Letters.
Exhibited NAD 1892, 1901–03, 1908, 1910–11, 1913, 1919–22, 1924–30, 1932–35, 1938–43, 1945.

ASHER B. DURAND (1796–1886)
(Founder NA 1826, PNA 1845–61)
The Morning of Life. 49¾ × 84 inches.
The Evening of Life. 49½ × 83¼ inches.
Both signed, A. B. Durand 1840.
National Academy of Design.
Gift of Mrs. Frederic H. Betts, 1911.

Durand left his native village of Jefferson, N. J. at the age of sixteen to become apprenticed to engraver Peter Maverick in Newark. In 1820 Durand decided to strike out on his own, and when he published his engraving of John Trumbull's painting, "The Declaration of Independence" in 1823, became one of the most sought after engravers in the country. Durand's business prospered, and he was able to buy for $600 John Vanderlyn's "Ariadne", a print of this first American nude adding to Durand's reputation. He was a founding member of the National Academy as an engraver, but his new acquaintance, Thomas Cole, urged him to give up printmaking and concentrate on painting. He executed a series of all the presidents up to that time, including Jackson, for Luman Reed, a generous New York patron. Durand studied in Europe in 1840–41 and returned to pursue landscape painting almost exclusively. His debt to Cole he acknowledged by painting "Kindred Spirits" to give to William Cullen Bryant as a tribute to their mutual friend, Cole, after the latter's death. Durand's long tenure as President of the National Academy was a tribute paid to him by his peers. His art was seen as a visual parallel to Emersonian morality by Henry Tuckerman, writing in *The Crayon*, who referred to it as a "vehicle of great moral impressions."
Exhibited NAD 1826–29, 1831–61, 1863–74, 1876.

Frank Duveneck, NA
Portrait of John W. Alexander, NA. Oil
Cincinnati Art Museum

FRANK DUVENECK (1848–1919)
(ANA 1905, NA 1906)
Portrait of John W. Alexander (c. 1879).
38 × 22⅛ inches.
Cincinnati Art Museum.

Duveneck was the son of German parents who
had immigrated to Covington, Kentucky. His
early art education was as an apprentice church
decorator in Cincinnati. At the age of twenty-two
he went to Munich to study at the Royal Academy where he shortly began to win student prizes
and was rewarded by being given a studio of his
own in 1872. Rich and brilliant brush work became his hallmark. He returned home in 1873,
and for the next two years his painting created a
sensation in Cincinnati and Boston. He returned
to Munich in 1875, starting his own school in 1878
with students of many nationalities, but mainly
American. Among them were Alexander, Chase,
DeCamp, Blum, and Twachtman. Duveneck
took his school to Florence in 1879, and students
shuttled back and forth from Florence to Venice,
winters and summers, for two years. He began to
etch in 1880 in Venice and shared a studio briefly
with Whistler to learn some of the older artist's
methods. He also worked at sculpture, one example of which, his recumbent bronze figure memorial to his bride of two years, has been widely
copied in marble and bronze. He returned to Cincinnati after his wife's death in 1888 and spent the
rest of his life there as a respected teacher at the
Cincinnati Art Institute. His painting never again
achieved the impact of his early promise.
Exhibited NAD 1877, 1879, 1888.

THOMAS EAKINS (1844–1916)
(ANA 1902, NA 1902)
Addie. 24⅛ × 18¼ inches. Signed, T. E. 1900.
Philadelphia Museum of Art.

Eakins graduated from high school in his native
city of Philadelphia and promptly enrolled in the
Pennsylvania Academy of the Fine Arts. He
studied there until the age of twenty-two. For the
following three years he received additional instruction from Gérôme, Bonnat, and the sculptor
Dumont at the École des Beaux-Arts, Paris.
Eakins then spent seven months, 1869–70, re-
cuperating from an illness in Spain. This brief
period probably had great influence on him because of his study of the Spanish masters, Velázquez, Ribera, and Goya. Late in 1870 he returned
to Philadelphia where he stayed, studying anatomy at the Jefferson Medical School. This specialty brought about an appointment to the faculty of the Pennsylvania Academy in 1873 and
his dismissal in 1886 for using a nude male model
in a mixed class. In 1875 his Rembrandt-inspired
painting of "The Gross Clinic" revolted the local
art public by its realism. His portraits, also, found
little approval because of his unrelieved honesty.
A meticulous craftsman in the Gérôme tradition,
Eakins had a wide ranging curiosity about physi-
ology, photography, mathematics, and athletics
in addition to superior skills in sculpture and painting. In 1884 he worked with Eadweard Muybridge in the study of motion in photography
with multiple cameras and successive plates. He
was a modest man, fluent in five languages and a
vigorous sportsman.
Exhibited NAD 1877–79, 1881–82, 1888, 1891–92,
1895–96, 1902, 1904–10, 1912–14, 1916.

Thomas Eakins, NA
Addie. Oil
Philadelphia Museum of Art

Charles Loring Elliott, NA
Mary Anne Goulding. Oil
National Academy of Design

CHARLES LORING ELLIOTT (1812–1868)
(ANA 1845, NA 1846)
Mary Anne Goulding. 34¼ × 27 inches. Signed,
Elliott 1858.
National Academy of Design.
Exhibited 1859. Gift of Samuel Goulding, 1901,
through S. P. Avery.

Elliott was discouraged by his architect father
from studying art, so he was forced to work in a
store for some years in his home town of Syracuse, New York. The father relented in 1834
and sent him off to New York to work under
Quidor. After a training period which included
some story illustrations, he set out on a ten-year
odyssey as an itinerant portrait painter through
the cities and college towns of the Northeast. By
1845 he had developed his skills to the point that
he became one of the most prolific and proficient
portraitists of his time. The names of his sitters
include notables from the political, academic, literary, and art worlds. With all his travel he evidently desired to paint only one landscape in
his life. His portraits have a generally solid simplicity done in an easy manner but without the
brush virtuosity of later artists. Stillman S. Co-
nant's obituary of Elliott in *The Galaxy* reads,
"His pictures were a true reflex of his own character." Mid-century attitudes linked art with the
character of the artist, and Elliott was admired
and well liked.
Exhibited NAD 1836, 1839–40, 1844–60, 1862–69.

FREDERICK FRIESEKE (1874–1939)
(ANA 1912, NA 1914)
Reclining Nude. 32 × 51 inches.
Signed, F. C. Frieseke, 1925.
Peter H. Davidson, New York.

Frieseke was born in Owosso, Michigan. At the
age of twenty he studied at The Art Institute of
Chicago, at twenty-one at the Art Students'
League in New York and at twenty-four at
Whistler's Académie Carmen in Paris. In 1899 he
painted mural decorations for Wanamaker's store
and the Shelbourne Hotel in Atlantic City.
Frieseke discovered Impressionism in France and
became an expatriate from 1905 until his death.
He won prizes and honors beginning at Munich in
1904, including over the years most of the major
expositions of Europe and the United States. In
1912 his painting "La Toilette" was accepted by
the Metropolitan Museum as a gift from Wanamaker. Dozens of other museums followed suit
and acquired their Friesekes. The nature of his
success can be measured by his receipt in 1920 of
two gold medals and the popular prize also at The
Art Institute of Chicago for a single painting
"Torn Lingerie." He is buried in France.
Exhibited NAD 1903, 1909, 1911–18, 1920–31,
1933–35, 1939–40.

Frederick Frieseke, NA
Reclining Nude. Oil
Peter H. Davidson, New York

George Fuller, NA
Winifred Dysart. Oil
Worcester Art Museum, Worcester, Massachusetts

GEORGE FULLER (1822–1884) (ANA 1853)
Winifred Dysart. 50⁷⁄₁₆ × 40½ inches. Signed,
G. Fuller.
Worcester Art Museum, Worcester,
Massachusetts. Exhibited NAD 1881.

Fuller had to struggle against family and financial odds. He was born into a farming family in Deerfield, Massachusetts. Because his parents were resistant to his interest in art, George worked at a variety of jobs, such as clerking and surveying, in addition to farming. Finally, on a tour through upstate New York in 1841 with his brother, a miniaturist, to paint portraits at $15 and $20 each, he demonstrated to his parents' satisfaction that he could succeed as an artist. He then studied in the Albany studio of sculptor Henry Kirke Brown during the winter of 1841–42 and went on to Boston the two succeeding winters to enroll in the Boston Artists' Association, farming each summer. He entered the National Academy in 1847, and spent the following decade largely in New York. In 1860 he went on a six month tour of Europe to see great art before settling down to full time farming because of his father's death. For the next fifteen years Fuller only painted in moments stolen from farm work. The farm failed, but in 1876 he succeeded completely with a show of a dozen portraits in Boston. The present painting is widely accepted as his masterpiece. It was hailed in 1881 as the hit of the National Academy Annual of that year. Mrs. Schuyler Van Rensselaer wrote in *Six Portraits*, "No more fascinating, haunting, individual figure has come from a contemporary hand."
Exhibited NAD 1849, 1852–57, 1860, 1868, 1878–81.

DANIEL GARBER (1880–1958)
(ANA 1910, NA 1913)
Winter Landscape by Addingham. 25 × 30 inches.
Signed, Daniel Garber 1911.
National Academy of Design.
Diploma painting, acquired 1914.

Garber was born in Manchester, Indiana, and first studied at the Cincinnati Art Academy. He later went to Philadelphia to work at the Pennsylvania Academy where he remained for six years as a student of Anshutz and Weir. After a period of study in Paris and Florence he settled in Lumberville, Pennsylvania, and painted its rural surroundings as his chief source of inspiration. He taught at the Pennsylvania Academy during most of his remaining professional years. In 1933 Garber received the popular prize at the Carnegie International, Pittsburgh.
Exhibited NAD 1907–28, 1930, 1932–36, 1938, 1940–41, 1947, 1959.

William Glackens, NA
Chez Mouquin. Oil
The Art Institute of Chicago

WILLIAM GLACKENS (1870–1938)
(ANA 1906, NA 1933)
Chez Mouquin. 48⅜₆ × 36¼ inches. Signed,
W. Glackens '05.
The Art Institute of Chicago.

Glackens was a high school classmate of John
Sloan and Albert C. Barnes. Three years after
graduation he became an artist-reporter for several newspapers, *The Press*, *The Record*, and *The
Public Ledger*. Among his colleagues were Luks,
Sloan, and Shinn. He studied painting at the
Pennsylvania Academy between assignments and
came under the sway of Henri, who had just returned to Philadelphia to preach the gospel after
Manet, Velázquez, Hals, and Goya. In 1895 Henri
and Glackens left for an eighteen-month cycling
jaunt through France, Belgium, and Holland. On
his return Glackens moved to New York where
he did comic sketches for *The World* and artist-
reporting for *The Herald*. He then branched off
into magazine and book illustration but after 1905
was able to concentrate mainly on his painting.
With his Philadelphia expatriates he exhibited as a
member of "The Eight" in 1908, along with A. B.
Davies, Lawson, and Prendergast. Glackens was
part of the force behind the first Independents
show in 1910 and chaired the jury for American
submissions to the Armory Show of 1913. He was
the original adviser to his boyhood friend, Albert
C. Barnes, in selecting paintings for the remarkable Barnes Collection in Merion, Pennsylvania.
Exhibited NAD 1905, 1907–11, 1915, 1930, 1935,
1939–40.

GEORGE GROSZ (1893–1959) (ANA 1950)
Self Portrait. 24 × 20 inches. Signed, Grosz, 1937
(on back).
National Academy of Design.

Grosz, a native of Berlin, started at age seventeen
to draw caricatures for the *Berliner Tageblatt*. A
year earlier he had enrolled in the Dresden Academy of Fine Arts where he continued to study for
two years, followed by a period at the Berlin
School of Applied Arts. In 1914 he was a soldier
at the front and in 1915 was hospitalized for shell
shock and began to resume his career as a carica-
turist. His reputation had preceded him when, in
1917, he was called up again by the Army and rejected as mentally unstable. "I returned to my four
walls, choking with hate," said Grosz. "I saw no
sense in this madness, only a world gone blind and
delirious." This hate, born of war's insanity, ener-
gized his work for the next fifteen years. Grosz
joined the Dadaists, edited a magazine whose third
number was confiscated by the police, and published his famous "Ecce Homo" series of thirty
drawings featuring a gas-masked Christ on the
cross. Injustice, profiteering, and corruption were
his targets, and he pilloried the Nazis before they
came to power. He left Germany just months
ahead of Hitler's takeover to come to the United
States where he immediately found himself in a
controversy. John Sloan had secured his appointment to the faculty of the Art Students' League.
Jonas Lie objected because Grosz would not be a
"healthy influence." Grosz was hired because of
student pressure, and he taught there for many
years. He continued to do some social comment
drawing and painting, especially during the Second World War, but his old vigor had diminished.
Exhibited NAD 1940, 1944–45, 1950, 1960.

George Grosz, ANA
Self Portrait. Oil
National Academy of Design

Hamilton Hamilton, NA
Lady in Black. Oil
National Academy of Design

HAMILTON HAMILTON (1847–1928)
(ANA 1886, NA 1889)
Lady in Black (c. 1889). 24 × 18 inches.
Signed, Hamilton Hamilton.
National Academy of Design.

Hamilton was a native of Middlesex County, England, whose family emigrated to the United States and settled in Cowlesville, New York. Largely self-taught, at the age of twenty-five he opened a studio in Buffalo to paint portraits. In 1875 he explored the Rocky Mountains and painted the Laramie peaks. In 1878–79 he visited France and worked at Pont-Aven, Brittany. In 1881 he returned to this country and settled in New York, producing paintings and etchings. He was a member of the American Watercolor Society and the New York Etching Club.
Exhibited NAD 1881–92, 1894–95, 1899–1905, 1911–12, 1925, 1928.

JAMES M. HART (1828–1901)
(ANA 1858, NA 1859)
The Adirondacks. 40 × 67 inches.
Signed, James M. Hart 1861.
Mr. and Mrs. George J. Arden, New York.

Hart came to this country at the age of three from his native Scotland when his parents settled in Albany, N. Y. When he was fifteen, Hart was apprenticed to a sign painter of Albany. Later he switched to easel painting, concentrating on portraits. At twenty-two he followed the art path to Düsseldorf for three years to learn how to paint in a photographically exact manner with a generous admixture of sentimentality. Back home in Albany he remained a few years working out his own landscape style, but eventually New York held greater attractions. The newly rich citizens of the post Civil War era needed culture credentials, and the acquisition of Hart landscapes of rural New York delighted buyers in search of his kind of quiet fidelity to nature. One of his specialties was the painting of cows, of which he was quite proud, even though his older brother, William, used to joke, "Jamie is a guid mon, but he dinna ken much aboot coos." Hart exhibited in the principal galleries of New York, Boston, Philadelphia, and Baltimore. He was at one period Vice-President of the National Academy.
Exhibited NAD 1853–60, 1862, 1865, 1867–68, 1870–72, 1874–1901.

James M. Hart, NA
The Adirondacks. Oil
Mr. and Mrs. George J. Arden, New York

WILLIAM S. HASELTINE (1835–1900)
(ANA 1860, NA 1861)
Sunrise at Capri. 32 × 56 inches. Signed, WSH.
National Academy of Design. Gift of the
artist's daughter, Mrs. Helen Plowden, 1953.

Haseltine was the middle of three artist sons of
the Philadelphia painter, Elizabeth S. Haseltine.
He graduated from Harvard in 1854 and studied
briefly with Paul Weber in his native city. Later
that same year he went to Düsseldorf for additional study. In 1856 he set out with Leutze,
Whittredge, and Bierstadt up the Rhine Valley,
over the Alps to Italy. This resulted in an instant
love affair with Italy for Haseltine which lasted
until he died. After two years he returned home
to America, where he lived and worked in New
York until 1866. From then until the end of his
life he resided in Europe except for the four years
between 1895 and 1899. Most of that time he
lived in an Italian palazzo near Rome, from which
he occasionally sent back to the States paintings
with such titles as "Bay of Naples", "Ischia",
"Pontine Marshes", "Venice", and "Ruins of a
Roman Theatre, Sicily".
Exhibited NAD 1859–65, 1871–72, 1874, 1885–86.

CHILDE HASSAM (1859–1935)
(ANA 1902, NA 1906)
Church at Old Lyme, Connecticut. 36 × 32 inches.
Signed, Childe Hassam 1905/Oct. 17.
Albright–Knox Art Gallery, Buffalo.

Hassam was an active, sports minded young man
in his native Dorchester, Massachusetts. After high
school he worked in a wood engraving shop and
started to do illustrations. Evenings he drew at the
Boston Art Club. Beginning in 1883 Hassam spent
most of the next six years in Europe, primarily
Paris. He studied at the Julian Academy and had
a painting accepted in the Salon of 1887 and received medals in Paris and Munich. In 1889 he
opened a New York studio and made friends with
Weir, Twachtman, Robert Reid, and Willard
Metcalf. These artists formed the nucleus of "Ten
American Painters" of 1898, that first collective
excursion into Impressionism by Americans. The
decade of the 'Nineties was Hassam's most ener-
getic period, his New England heritage drawing
him to that part of the country for subject matter.
At first his painting away from the city continued
to have some of the strength of his earlier work,
but as the years passed, especially his final fifteen
in East Hampton, Long Island, his art somewhat
declined. Over the years Hassam produced etchings which were as concerned with shimmering
effects of light as were his paintings.
Exhibited NAD 1883, 1886–87, 1890, 1898–1928,
1930–36.

Childe Hassam, NA
Church at Old Lyme, Connecticut. Oil
Albright-Knox Art Gallery, Buffalo

CHARLES HAWTHORNE (1872–1930)
(ANA 1908, NA 1911)
The Captain's Wife (1924). 60 × 48 inches.
Forum Gallery, New York.

Hawthorne left his boyhood home in Richmond, Maine, at the age of eighteen to study art in New York. He worked in a stained glass factory while enrolled at the Art Students' League under F. V. DuMond and G. D. Brush. He also worked with W. M. Chase both at the League and at the Chase School which Hawthorne helped found. The school evolved into the New York School of Art, and Hawthorne not only taught there but was its manager for several years. A painting jaunt in Holland was his sole contact with Europe, although he was made a full member of the French Société Nationale des Beaux-Arts in 1913. By the turn of the century Hawthorne had discovered Provincetown at the tip of Cape Cod. Remembering his summer experiences with Chase, Hawthorne established the Cape Cod School of Art, adapting many of Chase's methods to his own perceptions and style. He painted the Portuguese fishing families in a straightforward manner, not unlike Henri's, which won Hawthorne many prizes (First Hallgarten Prize, National Academy, 1904; silver medal, Buenos Aires, 1910; Altman Prize and Isidor gold medal, National Academy, 1914; silver medal, Panama Pacific Exposition, 1915; and Harris Prize and bronze medal, The Art Institute of Chicago, 1917). Hawthorne's teaching style can be sampled in the posthumous collection of student memories of his aphorisms and methods entitled, *Hawthorne on Painting.*
Exhibited NAD 1900–13, 1920–21, 1923–26, 1928, 1930.

GEORGE P. A. HEALY (1813–1894) (HM(P) 1843)
Portrait of the Countess of Saint-Roman.
63 × 47 inches. Signed, G. P. A. Healy.
Schweitzer Gallery, New York.

Healy was early recognized in his native Boston as a young man of talent. Sully encouraged him, and a portrait commission from Mrs. Harrison Gray Otis while he was still in his teens attracted society sitters. At the age of twenty-one Healy left for Paris to begin a life of being a shuttling American art ambassador. He first studied in the studio of Baron Gros, then under Thomas Couture, who became one of his close friends. He remained in Paris for many years as a portrait painter, among his subjects being King Louis Philippe, United States Ambassador Louis Cass, François Guizot, and Léon Gambetta. In 1855 he received a medal in Paris for "Franklin Urging the Claims of the American Colonies before Louis XVI". That year he established a home and studio in Chicago, from which he traveled to the east coast and the southern states painting portraits of leading politicians and society leaders. After the Civil War he returned to Europe to stay for most of the next twenty-five years, though he visited the United States occasionally to execute portrait commissions. He was the first American to be invited to contribute a self-portrait to the Uffizi Gallery in Florence. At the age of seventy-nine Healy left Europe for good because he had become unsympathetic with the Parisian art scene. Exhibited NAD 1842, 1844, 1848, 1852, 1857–60, 1865, 1867–68, 1872–73, 1877, 1881–85, 1887.

Charles Hawthorne, NA
The Captain's Wife. Oil
Forum Gallery, New York

Robert Henri, NA
The Guide to Croagan. Oil
Kenneth Lux, New York

ROBERT HENRI (1865–1929)
(ANA 1905, NA 1906)
The Guide to Croagan. 41 × 33 inches.
Signed, Robert Henri.
Kenneth Lux, New York.

Henri was born Robert Henry Cozad in Cincinnati and raised largely in Nebraska and Colorado. His father killed a man in self-defense (affirmed by a coroner) and in order to separate themselves from a dubious past, the family adopted different names. Robert dropped the family surname and changed his middle name to the French form but with an American pronunciation—Hen-rye. In 1886 he entered the Pennsylvania Academy to study under Anshutz. Two years later he and other Philadelphia students went to Paris to work under Bouguereau and Fleury at the Julian Academy. In 1891 Henri returned to Philadelphia to teach, becoming the leader of a group of young artists who were destined shortly to shake up the art world. These were Sloan, Luks, Glackens, and Shinn, and they responded enthusiastically to Henri's creed to paint life, not dry academic history and mythology. The turn of the century found the restless Henri established in New York where he taught successively at five different schools, among them the Chase School, the Art Students' League, and his own school. He was a member of the Society of American Artists and, with them, later joined the National Academy. In spite of his leadership of the secessionist group who exhibited once only as "Eight American Painters" at the Macbeth Gallery, Henri never forsook the Academy. His pungent aphoristic teaching style can be discovered in his book, *The Art Spirit.*
Exhibited NAD 1898, 1903–10.

EDWARD L. HENRY (1841–1919)
(ANA 1867, NA 1869)
The Old Sign on Tenth Street. 11½ × 8¾ inches.
Signed, E. L. Henry, Feb., 1877.
National Academy of Design.

Henry was brought to New York City at the age of seven by his parents from Charleston, South Carolina. After receiving his basic schooling he attended the Pennsylvania Academy, following with studies in Paris under Suisse, Gleyre, and Courbet. Henry was a nostalgia buff who painted super-realistic, recreated illustrations of life in the first half of the nineteenth century. His needle-sharp renderings of places and situations often included large crowds of people, sometimes with tiny recognizable portraits, as in "The Reception to Lafayette". Henry's work was exhibited at the major national fairs and frequently won medals and prizes, i.e., Honorable Mention, Paris, 1889. Exhibited NAD 1861, 1863–72, 1874–1919.

Edward L. Henry, NA
The Old Sign on Tenth Street. Oil
National Academy of Design

THOMAS HICKS (1823–1890)
(ANA 1841, NA 1851)
Italian Landscape (c. 1848). 15 × 21 inches.
Signed.
National Academy of Design. Acquired
as part of the Suydam Collection, 1865.

Hicks started out in his native Bucks County,
Pennsylvania, to be a coach painter for a cousin,
but a portrait he did of his employer convinced
his father to let him study art. He first went to the
Pennsylvania Academy and then to the National
Academy of Design in New York. He was elected
an Associate of the Academy at the age of eighteen
largely because of his "Death of Abel". In 1845 he
toured Europe, London, Florence, and Rome and
finished with an extended stint in Couture's atelier.
Back home in 1849 he set up shop in New York
City as a portrait painter and attracted many of the
illustrious figures of his time as subjects. Among
them were Henry Ward Beecher, William Cullen
Bryant, Bayard Taylor, O. W. Holmes, H. W.
Longfellow, Harriet Beecher Stowe, General
Meade, Lincoln, Edwin Booth (as Iago), and
Stephen Foster. In addition he did historical sub-
jects and other romantic compositions.
Exhibited NAD 1839–45, 1847, 1850–59, 1861–91.

WINSLOW HOMER (1836–1910)
(ANA 1864, NA 1865)
The Gale. 30 ¼ × 48⁵⁄₁₆ inches. Signed,
Winslow Homer 1893.
Worcester Art Museum,
Worcester, Massachusetts.

Homer, born in Boston, learned the lithographer's
craft and then set out at the age of twenty-one to
be a free lance illustrator. He moved to New York
in 1859 and soon was supplying drawings to
Harper's Weekly for engravings. His name first
became widely known for his studies of Civil War
soldiers' life. He started to paint at this time, also,
and he became known as a genre painter of both
sophisticated and rural subjects. Homer was in
France for ten months during 1867, but there is no
evidence that this visit affected his art. However,
a two-year residence in Tynemouth, England, on
the northeast coast facing the tempestuous North
Sea seems to have been a crucial experience. He
painted a series of dramatic coastal compositions
which focussed on man's eternal struggle with the
sea. Homer was so profoundly affected by his
English experience that, immediately upon his return to the United States in 1883 he moved to the
closest American approximation to the English
coast that he could find, Prout's Neck, Scarbor-
ough, Maine. He built a house on the coast where
he could intensely observe the moods of sea
weather. Homer had begun to paint in watercolor
in 1873. During his brief excursions away from
Prout's Neck to the Adirondacks or during his
winter visits to Florida and the West Indies he
made maximum use of watercolor to record fugi-
tive impressions of nature and figures in action.
Exhibited NAD 1860, 1863–72, 1874–80, 1883–88,
1906, 1908, 1910–11.

Winslow Homer, NA
The Gale. Oil
Worcester Art Museum, Worcester, Massachusetts

Thomas Hovenden, NA
Old Negro Smoking a Pipe. Oil
John D. Rockefeller III, New York

THOMAS HOVENDEN (1840–1895)
(ANA 1881, NA 1882)
Old Negro Smoking a Pipe. 16 × 20 inches.
John D. Rockefeller III, New York.

Hovenden was an orphan from the age of six in his native Cork, Ireland. After an apprenticeship of seven years to a carver and gilder of Cork, his master sent him to the Cork School of Design for additional instruction. He embarked for this country in 1863 and quickly became a student at the National Academy School. In 1874 he went to Paris for six years where he studied with Cabanel at the École des Beaux-Arts. On his return to the United States he first located in New York, but soon transferred to Philadelphia to teach at the Pennsylvania Academy. Henri was one of his students. Hovenden's loyalty to and feeling for his adopted country is evident in his genre subjects, such as "The Last Moments of John Brown" and "Breaking Home Ties", possibly his best known work. He was particularly sympathetic in his handling of subjects involving Black Americans. His photographically influenced painting was typical of a whole era of artists who viewed the camera as a competitor which must be outdone. Hovenden was killed while trying to save a little girl from an oncoming railroad train in Norristown, Pa.
Exhibited NAD 1867–68, 1872, 1874, 1876–78, 1881–91, 1893–96.

DANIEL HUNTINGTON (1816–1906)
(ANA 1839, NA 1840, PNA 1877–91)
Self Portrait. 36 × 29 inches. Signed,
D. Huntington 1891.
National Academy of Design.
Received in 1893 in exchange
for portrait by C. Ver Bryck.

Huntington, a native New Yorker, went first to Yale in pursuit of a profession and then went to Hamilton College. There itinerant artist Charles L. Elliott painted his portrait for $5 and praised Huntington's own attempts. In 1836 he was back in New York City attending Morse's lectures at New York University and studying painting with Henry Inman. Shortly afterwards he entered the National Academy's school and, by the age of twenty-two, he had advanced sufficiently to have a portrait of his father hung on the line in the Annual of 1838. He also painted some Hudson River landscapes but soon transferred his activities to Europe in 1839 where he painted in Rome, Florence, and Paris. He went to Rome a second time in 1842 and stayed for three years. After more portrait commissions in New York he returned again to Europe in 1851, this time to England to visit the Crystal Palace and to paint portraits of such London notables as Sir Charles Eastlake, President of the Royal Academy, and the Earl of Carlisle. Huntington came back to the States in 1858 to pursue his portrait career at home. His presidency of the National Academy was the longest in its history. He painted about a thousand portraits plus two hundred other compositions during his long life.
Exhibited NAD 1836–1901, 1903, 1905.

George Inness, NA
The Rainbow. Oil
Indianapolis Museum of Art

GEORGE INNESS (1825–1894)
(ANA 1853, NA 1868)
The Rainbow. 30 × 45 inches.
Indianapolis Museum of Art.

Inness was born in Newburgh, New York, and spent his youth in Newark, New Jersey. His father was a merchant who tried at first to discourage his son from studying art. Young Inness was even given a grocery store by his father to run at the age of fourteen. It lasted a month. He went to work for a map engraver in New York City in 1841. This lasted not much longer. Impatient with rules and preconceptions in art, Inness started to paint alone. He progressed well enough that he exhibited at the National Academy in 1844 and the following year at the American Art-Union. One more brief stint of instruction Inness tolerated in 1846 with the immigrant Frenchman, Régis Gignoux, from whom he only wanted some knowledge of oil painting technique. A month of that, also, was sufficient. By 1847 a dealer was sufficiently impressed with Inness's skills to send him to Europe for a year's study, primarily in the museums, and trips to Europe became a regular feature of his life. Most of his career he was often in need, but by his middle years he began to reap the rewards of his long struggle with the problems of landscape painting. The decade following the Civil War was perhaps Inness's best period. He had given up his early focus on the Hudson River School as his model and had introduced his own sense of structure and atmospheric color into his work.
Exhibited NAD 1844–50, 1852–53, 1855–60, 1862–63, 1865, 1867–72, 1874–75, 1877–79, 1881–83, 1885–86, 1888–89.

JOHN B. IRVING (1826–1877)
(ANA 1869, NA 1872)
Old Church, Düsseldorf. 17 × 14 inches.
Signed, 1873.
National Academy of Design.

Irving went to Düsseldorf in 1851 to study under Emanuel Leutze after a period of study in his native city of Charleston, South Carolina. He returned to the United States after a few years to establish himself as a portraitist in his home town. The Civil War disrupted that plan, and Irving moved to New York following Appomattox. Although he continued for a while in his portrait career (the August Belmonts and John Jacob Astor were among his subjects), his main interest became genre and historical compositions. In these latter works his detailed style was influenced by the French painter, Meissonier. A benefit exhibition for the artist's family was held at the Belmont home after Irving's death.
Exhibited NAD 1867–77.

John B. Irving, NA
Old Church, Düsseldorf. Oil
National Academy of Design

EASTMAN JOHNSON (1824–1906)
(ANA 1859, NA 1860)
On the Way to Camp. 19 × 30 inches.
Signed, E. Johnson, 1873.
Mr. and Mrs. Clyde Newhouse, New York.

Johnson, a native of Maine, went to Boston at sixteen to train as a lithographer in the same shop, Bufford's, where Winslow Homer would later get his start. For most of the 1840's Johnson made a living doing crayon portraits in Augusta, Maine, Cambridge, Massachusetts, Newport, Rhode Island, and Washington, D. C. In the national capitol he set up shop to draw in a Senate committee room. In 1849 he went to Düsseldorf to study under Leutze, then traveled to Italy and France. It was his four years' residence in The Hague, however, that provided him with a technique which he adapted to his own needs. In this he succeeded so well he was offered the position of painter to the Dutch court which he refused. In 1858 Johnson established a studio in New York and shortly his reputation as a painter of appealing genre subjects began to spread and satisfied the demand for themes like "Old Kentucky Home", "Husking Bee", and "Cranberry Pickers". In addition the list of his portrait sitters reads like a contemporary Who's Who. J. Q. Adams, Webster, Longfellow, Emerson, Cleveland, Arthur, Harrison, Vanderbilt, and Edwin Booth are on the roster. His art continued to mature with the years so that Sadakichi Hartmann could write, "His self-portrait, painted in 1899, is technically superior to anything executed by him during the first fifty years of his life."
Exhibited NAD 1856–57, 1859–62, 1865–90, 1892–93, 1895, 1898–1900.

JOHN F. KENSETT (1818–1872)
(ANA 1848, NA 1849)
Mountain Stream. 36 × 29 inches. Signed, initials, 1855.
National Academy of Design.
Acquired in 1865 as part of the Suydam Collection.

Kensett was the son of an English immigrant engraver who lived in Cheshire, Connecticut, and early learned his father's trade at home. After 1829, when his father died, Kensett continued his engraving education with his uncle. He then went to work for the American Bank Note Company in New York City. While there he met Thomas B. Rossiter and other artists who convinced him that he had talent which would find a better outlet in painting. In 1840 Kensett accompanied Rossiter, Asher B. Durand, and John W. Casilear on a trip to Europe. He stayed for seven years, traveling through England, France, Germany, and Italy. Kensett was impressed with "the stately woods of Windsor and the famous beeches of Burnham and the lovely and fascinating landscape that surrounds them." He went on a sketching tour with Benjamin Champney, an American whom he met in Paris, up the Rhine through Switzerland to Italy. Kensett's reputation was already made by the time he returned to New York in 1847. He had been sending home canvases from his European jaunt, and he soon was regarded as one of America's best landscape painters. He traveled from the New England coast to Colorado in search of material for his cool, sharply observed paintings and from these sketches spent the winters in his New York City studio turning them into finished landscapes.
Exhibited NAD 1838, 1845, 1847–63, 1865–73.

John F. Kensett, NA
Mountain Stream. Oil
National Academy of Design

Karl Knaths, NA
Kit and Kin. Oil
The Phillips Collection, Washington, D.C.

KARL KNATHS (1891–1971) (ANA 1968, NA 1971)
Kit and Kin (1947). 40 × 50 inches. Signed,
Karl Knaths.
The Phillips Collection, Washington, D. C.

Son of German and Austrian immigrants, Knaths
was born in Eau Claire, Wisconsin, where he
spent his early years. He received his art education
at the Milwaukee Art Institute and The Art Institute of Chicago. He earned his way with various
odd jobs, busboy, janitor's helper, and as a painter
of stage scenery, box cars, and railroad switches.
After his five years (1913–1918) in Chicago he
came east to settle in Provincetown, Massachusetts, where he lived for the rest of his life. A simple man with simple tastes, he built his own house
and lived a modest, congenial life at the tip of
Cape Cod. Knaths' career was, however, one of
the more honored of recent artists. Beginning in
1930 he had frequent one-man exhibitions at galleries and museums of the United States. Duncan
Phillips became a principal supporter and collected
over forty of his canvases. His work is located in
the leading museums of the country, notably the
Whitney Museum, Museum of Modern Art, and
the museums of Philadelphia, Detroit, Chicago,
Worcester, and Buffalo. He also taught at leading
eastern educational institutions.
Exhibited at the National Academy 1947–8, 1956,
1962–9, 1971.

JOHN LAFARGE (1835–1910)
(ANA 1863, NA 1869)
Greek Love Token. 24 × 13 inches.
Signed, La Farge, 1866.
National Collection of Fine Arts,
Washington, D. C.

LaFarge was born and raised in New York in an
intellectual French Catholic family. He graduated from Mt. St. Mary's College in Maryland at
the age of eighteen. Paris, beginning in 1856, provided his art education. He studied with Couture
and in the museums and in London was much impressed by the Pre-Raphaelites. Upon his return
to the United States in 1858 LaFarge continued
Couture-like studies with one of the master's
pupils, William M. Hunt, at Newport, Rhode
Island. Rejected for service in the Civil War for
nearsightedness, he decided to concentrate on
painting. By 1876 his career had developed sufficiently that he was invited by H. H. Richardson
to paint murals for the architect's Trinity Church,
Boston. This was followed by other church commissions, and LaFarge became one of the leaders
of the mural movement of the late 19th century.
He was also well acquainted with the contemporary literati. Henry James and Henry Adams were
among his friends, and in 1886 LaFarge traveled
with the latter to Japan and Southeast Asia. He
became an expert stained glass designer and received the Legion of Honor in Paris, 1889, for one
of his windows. His fame in this craft derives from
his invention of opaline glass and his design ability. LaFarge also wrote and lectured extensively
on art.
Exhibited NAD 1862–64, 1867–71, 1874–76, 1878–
79, 1887, 1893, 1895, 1908.

John LaFarge, NA
Greek Love Token. Oil
National Collection of Fine Arts, Washington, D.C.

ERNEST LAWSON (1873–1939)
(ANA 1908, NA 1917)
Morningside Heights. 34½ × 40½ inches.
Signed, E. Lawson.
Mr. and Mrs. George J. Arden, New York.

Lawson was born of Canadian parents in San
Francisco and spent his boyhood in Kansas City.
There he received his first art instruction, in tex-
tile design from a traveling salesman. When he
was sixteen the family moved to Mexico City. He
saved up enough to go to New York to study at
the Art Students' League in 1890 under Twachtman and also worked with both Twachtman and
Weir at Cos Cob, Connecticut. In 1893 he went
to France for a brief period of study at the Julian
Academy. The next decade was spent in New
York, the longest time he ever spent in any one
place. In 1898 he moved to Washington Heights,
the locale which provided him with subjects for
many of his first successful works. Beginning with
the winter of 1903–04 in France, he spent a great
deal of his life being a global roamer—Spain,
New York, Nova Scotia, Long Island, Kansas
City, France, Tennessee, Connecticut, finishing in
Florida. Lawson stayed in New York City long
enough at one stretch 1908–1913 to participate in
the exhibitions of "The Eight", the first "Independents", and the "Armory Show" but he was
less committed to organizing revolutions than
exhibiting his quiet brand of late Impressionist
urban and rural landscapes. He drowned near
Miami. The coroner decided suicide. His friends
believed otherwise.
Exhibited NAD 1905–1939.

EMANUEL LEUTZE (1816–1868)
(HM(P) 1843, NA 1860)
Portrait of Worthington Whittredge. 30¼ × 25 inches.
Signed, 1861.
National Academy of Design.

Leutze was brought to the United States from his
native Germany as an infant, the family first settling in Fredericksburg, Virginia, then in Philadelphia where Leutze received his art instruction.
His early experience was as a portrait and figure
painter, this work so impressing his fellow Phila-
delphians that he gained the patronage of E. L.
Carey and others which enabled him to go to
Düsseldorf for further study. This was in 1841,
and he stayed until 1859. During this period
Leutze first studied with K. F. Lessing and subsequently became a kind of "lieber meister" for
many young American artists. He turned his attention to historical painting and did two versions
of "Washington Crossing the Delaware" by 1851
(the first was partially destroyed in a fire). The
precision of his Düsseldorf skills and his evident
patriotism were just what American official taste
wanted. The last nine years of his life were busily
occupied shuttling between New York and
Washington, D. C. painting such works as
"Westward the Course of Empire Takes its Way"
in the House of Representatives, "The Landing of
the Norsemen", "The Settlement of Maryland",
"Washington at Monmouth", and "Signing of
the Alaska Purchase Treaty". Leutze also painted
portraits of Grant, Hawthorne, Burnside and
other notables.
Exhibited NAD 1843, 1845–47, 1849, 1852, 1857–
58, 1860–61, 1863, 1865, 1867–71.

Emanuel Leutze, NA
Portrait of Worthington Whittredge, NA. Oil
National Academy of Design

Reginald Marsh, NA
High Yaller. Tempera on board
Alfred Easton Poor, PNA, New York

REGINALD MARSH (1898–1954)
(ANA 1937, NA 1943)
High Yaller. 17½ × 23½ inches.
Signed, Reginald Marsh, 1934.
Alfred Easton Poor, PNA, New York

Marsh was born in Paris of American artist parents. From the age of two he grew up in New Jersey and began his art career as art editor and cartoonist for the *Yale Record.* On graduation from Yale in 1920 he worked as staff artist for *Vanity Fair* and the *New York Daily News.* He held his first one-man show in 1924 at the Whitney Studio Club. He worked briefly for the *New Yorker* and then went to Europe to study the old masters in order to develop the skill necessary to depict modern life in old masterly technique. In 1926 he returned and enrolled at the Art Students' League to study under John Sloan, George Luks, Kenneth Hayes Miller and Boardman Robinson. He painted murals for the Post Office Building in Washington, D. C., and for the New York Customs House, but he was primarily an easel painter, etcher and lithographer of New York City life. The country bored him. Burlesque theaters, subways, Coney Island and the Bowery were Marsh's life blood.
Exhibited NAD 1927, 1935–41, 1944–47, 1949, 1952, 1954–55.

HENRY LEE MCFEE (1886–1953)
(ANA 1948, NA 1950)
Still Life. 25 × 30 inches.
National Academy of Design.

McFee was a native of St. Louis who studied art at Washington University after public schooling. In 1908 he came east to study with Birge Harrison at the Art Students' League in Woodstock, New York, and at the Stevenson Art Center, Philadelphia. Beginning in 1915 at the Panama-Pacific Exposition McFee's painting steadily climbed in public and critical esteem. He won honorable mention at the Carnegie International, 1923, the First Honorable Mention at the same exhibition, 1930, the fourth Clarke prize, Corcoran Gallery, 1928, the purchase prize at the Virginia Museum of Fine Arts, 1935, the Temple gold medal at the Pennsylvania Academy, 1937, and purchase prizes at the Los Angeles County Fair 1940 and 1949. McFee also was awarded a Guggenheim Fellowship, 1941, and was a member of the National Institute of Arts and Letters. His carefully crafted still lifes and interiors can be seen in major museums.
Exhibited NAD 1944–45, 1947, 1949, 1951.

GARI MELCHERS (1860–1932)
(ANA 1904, NA 1906)
Study of Dutch Types (*Heads and Hands*).
17½ × 26¾ inches.
National Academy of Design.

Melchers was born in Detroit and had the support of his sculptor-father who sent him, at the age of seventeen, to Düsseldorf to study at the Royal Academy under Edouard von Gebhardt. Four years later he enrolled in the École des Beaux-Arts in Paris and later studied with Boulanger and Lefebvre. He learned so well that by 1882 his painting, "The Letter", was accepted in the Salon of that year. After a trip to the United States and back to Paris, he then settled in Egmond, Holland, where he lived until 1914. If the guns of August had not sounded, he might have remained. Melchers's career was an endless success story, and he won many awards and honors. Over the door of his Dutch studio was the inscription "Waar en Klaar" (True and Clear), a reference to his attitude towards painting. His genre paintings of peasant types have a clarity and simplicity characteristic of Dutch painting. His paintings can be found in the Luxembourg Museum, Paris, and in the principal museums of the United States.
Exhibited NAD 1904, 1906, 1925, 1930.

FRANCIS D. MILLET (1846–1912)
(ANA 1881, NA 1885)
Queen of the Feast. 60 × 28 inches. Signed on the back, 1884.
National Academy of Design.
Exhibited as "Regina Convivia", 1886, Diploma painting.

Millet was born in Mattapoisett, Massachusetts. After drummer boy service in the Union Army he enrolled in Harvard College and graduated in 1869 with a degree in modern languages and literature. He reported for the Boston *Advertiser*, learned lithography, and went to Antwerp, Belgium, to study painting at the Royal Academy. In two years he had won all their prizes and was publicly honored by the king. Millet formed a friendship with Charles Francis Adams when they both worked on the Vienna Exposition in 1873. Millet then studied painting in Rome and Venice. He returned to become a correspondent for the *Advertiser* at the Philadelphia Centennial, 1876, where he also exhibited. He assisted LaFarge in painting the Trinity Church murals in Boston. He was a member of the international jury at the Paris Exposition of 1878 and exhibited at both the Salon and the British Royal Academy. He published short stories, travel pieces, war reports, and a translation of Tolstoy's *Sebastopol*. He was war correspondent in the Philippines, 1898, for the *London Times*, *Harper's Weekly*, and the *New York Sun*. Millet painted murals in the state capitols of Minnesota and Wisconsin and went on a special mission for war secretary Elihu Root to Japan in 1908. Millet was one of the many talents lost in the sinking of the Titanic.
Exhibited NAD 1876–77, 1879–1900, 1902, 1904, 1907.

Louis H. C. Moeller, NA
Home Again. Oil
National Academy of Design

LOUIS H. C. MOELLER (1855–1930)
(ANA 1884, NA 1895)
Home Again. 30 × 48 inches.
Signed, Louis Moeller.
National Academy of Design. Exhibited 1894.

Moeller was a native of New York who received his first art instruction from his father. He then attended classes at the National Academy school, after which he went to Munich to study under Frank Duveneck and Feodor Dietz for six years. On his return to New York he opened a studio and did decorative painting while he developed the genre painting style with which his name is associated. His first painting submitted to the Academy, "Girl in a Snow-Storm", was accepted, and his second, "Puzzled", earned him the Hallgarten prize and his nomination as an Associate of the Academy. From then on he became one of the better known painters of daily life of his period. Exhibited NAD 1883–89, 1891–98, 1908.

SAMUEL F. B. MORSE (1791–1872)
(Founder NA 1826, PNA 1826–45, 1861–62)
The Marquis de Lafayette (1824). 96 × 64 inches.
Signed, Morse.
Art Commission of the City of New York.

Morse was a native of Charlestown, Massachusetts, and went to England in 1811 to study under the expatriate Americans, Washington Allston and Benjamin West. He started out in his career with both a painting and a sculpture of the same subject, "The Dying Hercules". Neither elicited a hint of fame and fortune, so Morse turned to portrait painting for survival in 1815 and became one of the young nation's best early portraitists. He also painted panoramic interiors like "The House of Representatives" with its eighty-six portraits of legislators and "The Exhibition Gallery of the Louvre" with its walls crowded with over thirty recognizable masterworks. In 1829 he went on a commissioned trip to Europe to make copies and to paint views of the continent for American customers. After 1832 his interest waned as he began his electrical experiments. In 1839 he invented the telegraph and introduced photography to this country simultaneously. Morse's wealth increased, but his interest in art remained active through his continued presence as President of the National Academy. Exhibited NAD 1826–37, 1868–70.

Samuel F. B. Morse, PNA
The Marquis de Lafayette. Oil
Art Commission of the City of New York

WILLIAM S. MOUNT (1807–1868)
(ANA 1831, NA 1832)
Eel Spearing at Setauket. 29 × 36 inches.
Signed, Wm. S. Mount/1845.
New York State Historical Association,
Cooperstown.

Mount was a farmer's son whose entire life was associated with his native Setauket, L. I. At the age of seventeen he went to work for his older brother who was a sign painter in New York City. Mount studied engravings of the masters and was particularly impressed by the work of Benjamin West. He was one of the National Academy's first students of drawing in 1826, but ill health forced him to return to Setauket the following year. There he painted his first canvases which were exhibited at the National Academy in 1828, a self-portrait and two Biblical narratives. The quiet humor of his genre paintings endeared his work to his contemporaries. Charles Lanman wrote that they were "so comically conceived that they always cause the beholder to smile, whatever may be his troubles." Succeeding generations, however, have come to realize that Mount's achievement rests in his paint, not in his point. He also did many portraits, but these were less successful. Mount never traveled abroad. He quietly plowed his home fields and produced a genial, technically superior, body of work. During his last decade the state of his health prevented his doing much painting.
Exhibited NAD 1828–1869.

JEROME MYERS (1867–1940)
(ANA 1920, NA 1929)
Summer Night, East Side Park (1919).
25 × 30 inches. Signed, Jerome Myers.
Whitney Museum of American Art, New York.

Myers was born in Petersburg, Virginia, and raised in Philadelphia, Trenton, and Baltimore. At the age of nineteen he came to New York, fell in love with the city, and stayed for the rest of his life. His first New York professional experience was in the theater, both as an actor and as a scene painter. He studied art at Cooper Union and at the Art Students' League. Myers's principal teacher was George DeForest Brush, but the influence seems to have been slight because his real classroom was the streets of New York, from Chinatown to Central Park. In 1896 he made a brief foray to Paris, but New York's raffishness was his preference. His first one-man show was held in 1908 at William Macbeth's Gallery. Sloan wanted Henri to include Myers among "The Eight" of that year, but Henri considered Myers too soft and sentimental. He exhibited, however, in the Armory Show of 1913. He won a bronze medal in St. Louis, 1904, the Clarke Prize at the National Academy, 1919, and the National Academy's second Altman Prize in both 1931 and 1937, its Carnegie Prize in 1936, and its Isidor Prize, 1938. The Metropolitan Museum, the Whitney Museum, The Art Institute of Chicago, the Brooklyn Museum, the Corcoran Gallery, and the Phillips Gallery own his work.
Exhibited NAD 1902, 1905–11, 1914, 1916–41.

John Neagle, ʜᴍ(ᴘ)
Pat Lyon at the Forge. Oil
Owned by the Boston Anthenaeum,
lent through the Museum of Fine Arts, Boston

JOHN NEAGLE (1796–1865)
(ARTIST 1827, HM(P) 1828)
Pat Lyon at the Forge—exhibited NAD 1830.
93 × 68 inches. Signed, J. Neagle 1826 & 7.
Owned by The Boston Athenaeum.
Lent through the Museum of Fine Arts, Boston.

Neagle, a native of Boston, studied in Philadelphia
with Pietro Ancora, Thomas Wilson and Bass
Otis. After a journey through Kentucky to New
Orleans he returned to Philadelphia to set up a
portrait studio in 1818. Influenced by Sully and
Stuart, Neagle became well-regarded for his use
of color. His portrait of Stuart in 1825 is clearly
a superior achievement. The following year he
painted the present excellent canvas of Pat Lyon,
a successful Philadelphia manufacturer who
wanted to be remembered as the Irish workman
he started by being, instead of the wealthy middle-
class man he became. As a young locksmith Lyon
had been falsely sent to prison by perjured testi-
mony and he would have nothing further to do
with people of wealth. Neagle also painted James
F. Cooper, Henry Clay and other notables.
Exhibited NAD 1827, 1830, 1835, 1838.

VICTOR NEHLIG (1830–1909)
(ANA 1863, NA 1870)
Faust and Mephistopheles (c. 1870). 30 × 25 inches.
National Academy of Design.

Nehlig was a native of Paris and studied art there
under Cogniet and Abel de Pujol. At the age of
twenty he emigrated to the United States and
settled in New York. After a stay of twenty-two
years, during which he painted interpretations of
American history, both of the distant and recent
past, he returned to Europe. The titles of his
American paintings reveal his interests: "Poca-
hontas," "Hiawatha", "Gertrude of Wyoming",
"Battle of Antietam", "Battle of Gettysburg",
"Cavalry Charge of Lieutenant Hidden". The
last named canvas is in the possession of the New
York Historical Society.
Exhibited NAD 1862–63, 1870–71, 1888.

MAXFIELD PARRISH (1870–1966)
(ANA 1905, NA 1906)
Saint Valentine. 20 × 16 inches.
Signed twice, Maxfield Parrish, 1904.
National Academy of Design. Exhibited 1925.

Parrish was born into a Philadelphia Quaker family and received a thorough education which included three years (1882–85) in France and England, Haverford College, and finally the Pennsylvania Academy of Fine Arts. His aesthetic choices were largely the result of Philadelphia medievalism, which also produced Howard Pyle, Abbey, and the Wyeths. In 1895 Parrish moved to New Hampshire permanently and turned out a massive amount of magazine covers, posters, book illustrations, advertisements, calendar pictures, paintings, and murals. He was one of the most successful commercial artists in history whose combination of wit, sentimentality and fictitious Olden Tymes invaded almost every home in the United States by one means or another. It all started with a cover for *Harper's Weekly* in 1895, and it has not stopped yet. In the early 1900's his reputation as a painter was recognized by an honorable mention in Paris, 1900, a silver medal at the Pan-American Exposition, Buffalo the following year, and membership in the Society of American Artists and the National Academy. As a reflection of recent interest in Pop Art and nostalgia, Parrish has been seen as an antecedent of these attitudes in art, and was given retrospective exhibitions at Bennington College, Vermont, and the Gallery of Modern Art, New York, in 1964. He received honorary degrees from Haverford College and the University of New Hampshire.
Exhibited NAD 1909, 1925, 1930.

WILLIAM M. PAXTON (1869–1941)
(ANA 1917, NA 1928)
The New Necklace. 35½ × 28½ inches. Signed, Paxton/1910.
Museum of Fine Arts, Boston.

Paxton was a native of Baltimore who went to Paris to study at the École des Beaux-Arts under Gérôme. He returned to New York and studied additionally with Mrs. Jack Gardner's protegée, Denis Bunker. It was perhaps this association which drew him to Boston, but his particular brand of quiet, well-to-do interiors with figures influenced by Vermeer, filtered through the eyes of Philip Hale, could be located only on Beacon Hill. He won popular prizes at exhibitions in Detroit and at the Corcoran Gallery, Washington. At one moment, at the St. Botolph Club, Boston, 1905, he showed paintings which professed to represent the world as seen with binocular, instead of monocular vision. His method to do this was to paint duplicate edges and lines resulting in a blurred image.
Exhibited NAD 1911–13, 1917, 1920–34, 1936–39, 1941.

William M. Paxton, NA
The New Necklace. Oil
Museum of Fine Arts, Boston

HENRY VARNUM POOR (1888–1970)
(ANA 1948, NA 1963)
March Snow. 32 × 27¾ inches.
Signed, H. V. Poor.
Worcester Art Museum, Worcester,
Massachusetts.

Poor was born in Chapman, Kansas, and was first
interested in his high school shop course as a possible career. He entered Stanford University to
study economics, but remained for only one year.
He decided to switch to art, and his father decided
not to pay for it. Poor earned his way farming and
lumbering in the summers. He was an excellent
athlete and student, graduating Phi Beta Kappa in
1910. That summer he cycled through Europe to
visit museums and galleries. He then studied at
London's Slade School and under Walter Sickert.
Back home, he taught at Stanford University and
Hopkins Institute from 1911 until drafted into the
War in 1918. He exhibited once or twice after the
War, but in 1920 he moved to New City, New
York, built a stone house, and set up shop as a potter. Pottery was the basis of his first reputation, but
he returned to painting in 1929. He went to Mar-
seille, France for a year to renew his painting
skills and had his first New York solo show at the
Montross Gallery, 1931. He subsequently won
many awards for his painting and his ceramics.
Poor also became an excellent muralist in true
fresco technique, with panels in the Departments
of Justice and Interior, Washington, and at Pennsylvania State University, State College, Pennsylvania. He is represented in major American
museums.
Exhibited NAD 1927, 1946–49, 1962–63, 1965,
1968, 1971.

HENRY PRELLWITZ (1865–1940)
(ANA 1906, NA 1912)
Nausicaa (c. 1912). 24 × 36 inches. Signed,
Henry Prellwitz.
National Academy of Design.
Exhibited NAD 1912, acquired 1912,
Diploma painting.

Prellwitz was born in New York City and, after
basic schooling, studied with Thomas Dewing
and at the Art Students' League. He then went to
Paris to enroll at the Julian Academy. Upon his
return he won the Third Hallgarten Prize at the
National Academy, 1893, the bronze medal at the
Pan-American Exposition, Buffalo, 1901, a medal
at St. Louis, 1904, and the Clarke Prize, National
Academy, 1907. In 1906 he joined the Society of
American Artists just before that organization re-
united with the National Academy of Design. For
many years he taught at Pratt Institute, Brooklyn.
Exhibited NAD 1905, 1907, 1910, 1912–13, 1915,
1917, 1925, 1930–32, 1939, 1941.

Frederic Remington, ANA
Fired On! Oil
National Collection of Fine Arts, Washington, D. C.

FREDERIC REMINGTON (1861–1909) (ANA 1891)
Fired On! (c. 1907). 27⅛ × 40⅛ inches.
Signed, Frederic Remington.
National Collection of the Fine Arts,
Washington, D. C.

Remington was born at Canton, New York, and educated in Vermont and at the Yale School of Fine Arts. After graduation he traveled West, returning to study at the Art Students' League in New York. During his year in the plains states he worked as a cowboy, ranch hand, and lumberjack. This vigorous experience excited him, and he determined to become an illustrator, especially of outdoor life in the West. During the Spanish-American War he was an artist-correspondent in Cuba. In particular Remington drew horses in action wherever he found them, with rider or without, in the cities or open country. He studied Muybridge's book of photographs, "The Horse in Motion", and took photos himself with the newly invented roll film box camera. He illustrated articles by Theodore Roosevelt in *Century Magazine* in 1888. The following year he was awarded a silver medal at the Paris Exposition. He illustrated *Hiawatha*, Parkman's *Oregon Trail*, and books by Owen Wister, the writer who, with his novel, *The Virginian*, established the format of the American Western. In 1895 Remington started producing sculpture as a three-dimensional transformation of his drawings. His first, "The Bronco Buster", is one of his best. He wrote and illustrated seven books. His name is associated with the Old West as its preeminent recorder.
Exhibited NAD 1887–92, 1894–96, 1899.

T. ADDISON RICHARDS (1820–1900)
(ANA 1848, NA 1851)
New Hampshire Landscape (1851). 30¼ × 43 inches.
Signed, T. Addison Richards.
Mr. and Mrs. George J. Arden, New York.

Richards was the son of a Baptist minister of London, England, who emigrated with his family to the United States in 1831. They lived for four years in Hudson, New York, and then moved to the South, eventually to settle in Penfield, Georgia. At the age of twelve Richards wrote and illustrated in watercolor a manuscript volume of 150 pages about his trip from England. At eighteen he had a book on flower painting published under the title, *The American Artist*. He also painted portraits. In 1845 Richards went to New York City, studied under Daniel Huntington at the National Academy school for two years, and began to depict the Hudson River vicinity. The year following his election as an Academician he was named to the post of corresponding secretary of the National Academy, an office he kept for forty years, the period of the Academy's greatest growth and influence. He was widely traveled in the United States and Europe, and his illustrated handbook of American travel, published in 1857, is still a model of its kind. Just as his landscape painting was a factual representation of nature, his articles and travel books were as reliable guides as any Baedeker. Richards taught art at New York University and organized the first class for women at Cooper Union.
Exhibited NAD 1846–59, 1861–99.

Albert Pinkham Ryder, NA
Pegasus. Oil
Worcester Art Museum, Worcester, Massachusetts

ALBERT PINKHAM RYDER (1847–1917)
(ANA 1902, NA 1906)
Pegasus. 12 × 11⅜ inches. Inscribed in pencil on back of panel: Pegasus/Painted by Albert P. Ryder/for Charles deKay/1887.
Worcester Art Museum, Worcester, Massachusetts.

Ryder was a native of the seaport city of New Bedford, Massachusetts, who absorbed a little formal education and much sea lore there before leaving at the age of twenty with his parents for the city of New York. Ryder studied painting briefly with William E. Marshall and drawing in the antique classes of the National Academy. He made several trips to Europe, 1877, 1882, 1887 and 1896, but his primary interest seems to have been the sea voyages. His first paintings were memory landscapes of the New Bedford vicinity. In the 1880's he began to paint Biblical and mythological subjects. Wagnerian opera affected him profoundly, as did the Romantic poets and Shakespeare. Moderately successful, he lived a voluntarily humble existence, worked slowly (about 165 paintings in all), and ultimately has been paid the crass compliment of having his work forged to the total of five times his own output. A recluse in his late years, he died after a long illness at the home of friends in Elmhurst, Long Island.
Exhibited NAD 1873, 1876, 1881–84, 1886–88.

JOHN SINGER SARGENT (1856–1925)
(ANA 1891, NA 1897)
The Daughters of Edward Boit. 87 × 87 inches.
Signed, John S. Sargent 1882.
Museum of Fine Arts, Boston.

Sargent, son of a New England doctor, was born in Florence, Italy. An expatriate most of his life, he learned his dashing painting style from Carolus-Duran in his late 'teens. A visit to Spain in 1880, where he studied Velázquez, gave birth not only to the present painting (an echo of "Las Meninas") but to "El Jaleo" in the Gardner Museum, Boston, a sensation at the time it was first exhibited in 1882. "Madame X", shown in 1884, caused such a disturbance in Paris that Sargent was forced to move to London. In London Sargent had all the portrait commissions he could schedule and made friends with such other Americans as E. A. Abbey, Francis Millet, and Henry James. Interested in Impressionism, he visited and painted Monet at Giverny. Beginning in the early 1890's he embarked on a series of murals for the Boston Public Library which occupied him for twenty-five years. He also did a series for the Boston Museum of Fine Arts and one for the Widener Library at Harvard College. His last years he devoted to painting Impressionist watercolors of scenes and architecture on the continent. He was a member of the British Royal Academy and the French Legion of Honor. One of the most popular and proficient artists in the past hundred years, his work can be found in most of the museums of the country.
Exhibited NAD 1879, 1888–91, 1895–97, 1906–11, 1913, 1917, 1923, 1925.

John Singer Sargent, NA
The Daughters of Edward Boit. Oil
Museum of Fine Arts, Boston

Everett Shinn, NA
London Hippodrome. Oil
The Art Institute of Chicago

EVERETT SHINN (1876–1953)
(ANA 1935, NA 1943)
London Hippodrome (1902). 26⅜ × 35¼ inches.
Signed, E. Shinn.
The Art Institute of Chicago.

Shinn, a native of Woodstown, New Jersey, started as a mechanical engineer (he is credited with having invented the rotary engine), but was sacked from his job at a lighting fixture company for drawing a street scene in the margin of a huge detail drawing which bored him. Shinn then studied at the Pennsylvania Academy, met Luks, Sloan, Glackens, and Henri, and got a job as an artist-reporter for the Philadelphia *Press*. At the age of twenty he was first of the future Ashcan group to migrate to New York, where he drew free-lance for several newspapers and magazines. He exhibited oils and pastels of city subjects beginning in 1902, joined his friends of "The Eight" in 1908, and contributed to the Armory Show in 1913. Playwright Clyde Fitch and producer David Belasco became interested in Shinn, perhaps because of his ability as a playwright—he had written several comedy sketches which ultimately became standard vaudeville repertoire—but he, in turn, became interested in designing stage sets and decorative murals. Show business in all its guises fascinated Shinn. He painted pictures not only of the theater, but of the circus, the ballet and vaudeville. He was the art director for five motion pictures. His light touch was characteristic of both his life and his art. Examples of the latter can be found in major museums.
Exhibited NAD 1943–47, 1949–51, 1954.

WALTER SHIRLAW (1838–1909)
(ANA 1887, NA 1888)
The Toning of the Bell. 40 × 30 inches.
Signed, Walter Shirlaw 1874.
The Art Institute of Chicago.

Shirlaw was a native of Paisley, Scotland, and arrived in New York with his parents at the age of three. He first learned engraving during a five year apprenticeship and worked as a bank note engraver for a few years. He saved $800 and launched himself into a painting career. This lasted awhile, but the money ran out, and he had to return to bank note engraving during the late 1860's in Chicago. While there, Shirlaw participated in the establishment of The Art Institute of Chicago. Beginning in 1870 he studied in Munich for seven years and the present painting is from this period. Back in New York Shirlaw set to work as a portrait and genre painter and was soon involved in the founding of the Society of American Artists serving as its first president. He also taught at the Art Students' League. Much of his later career was occupied painting murals, designing stained glass windows, and illustrating for *Century* Magazine and *Harper's Monthly*. His murals were painted for private residences, for the Library of Congress, and for the World's Columbian Exposition in Chicago, 1893. He is represented in museums in St. Louis, Buffalo, Chicago, Washington, D. C., and Indianapolis.
Exhibited NAD 1861–63, 1877–79, 1881, 1883–92, 1894–96, 1898–99, 1903–08.

Walter Shirlaw, NA
The Toning of the Bell. Oil
The Art Institute of Chicago

WILLIAM L. SONNTAG (1822–1900)
(ANA 1860, NA 1861)
ARTHUR F. TAIT (1819–1905)
(ANA 1855, NA 1858)
Early Morning in the Adirondacks. 39 × 55 inches.
Signed, W. L. Sonntag A. F. Tait.
Mr. and Mrs. George J. Arden, New York.

Sonntag was a native of East Liberty, Pennsylvania, and early set out on a painting career as a landscapist. In a Cincinnati store front gallery Sonntag held an exhibition which attracted not only the attention of a director of the Baltimore and Ohio Railroad who commissioned Sonntag to paint a series of landscapes along the route of the B & O as it crossed the Alleghenies but also the attention of the future Mrs. Sonntag. The landscape assignment and the honeymoon coincided in a railroad trip with frequent stops to paint. After arriving in New York, the city became his home for life. There were regular summer jaunts to New England and twelve winters in Florence, Italy. There he painted American landscapes, not Italian. Sonntag created panoramas with John C. Wolfe representing Milton's "Paradise Lost" and "Paradise Regained", and with Arthur F. Tait he collaborated on several Catskill landscapes. He exhibited in many American cities, and his work is owned by the Corcoran Gallery and the Peabody Institute.
Exhibited NAD 1855–1900.

Tait was a native of England who was almost completely self-taught. What knowledge and skill in art he acquired was the result of working in a picture dealer's shop and drawing casts at the Royal Manchester Institution. He also made certain to become familiar with locally available masterworks. Tait was thirty-one when he emigrated and settled in New York. Here the Adirondack Mountains became his regular summer habitat. His paintings featured birds and other wildlife, and in 1852 he began to sell his paintings to Currier and Ives for lithographic reproduction. The demand for his work was so great that by 1860 he could afford to move out of the city to Morrisania and let the new art dealers, Michael Knoedler and Samuel P. Avery, handle his custom. After 1882 Tait no longer frequented the Adirondacks. He moved to Yonkers and continued to turn out his popular small paintings of rural scenes with and without animals. Examples of his work are owned by the New York Historical Society, the Baltimore Museum, the Springfield Museum, Museum of Fine Arts, Boston, the Cleveland Museum, the Brooklyn Museum, and the Adirondack Museum.
Exhibited NAD 1852–63, 1865, 1867–74, 1876, 1878–1905.

Eugene Speicher, NA
Katharine Cornell. Oil
Albright-Knox Art Gallery, Buffalo
Julia R. and Estelle L. Foundation

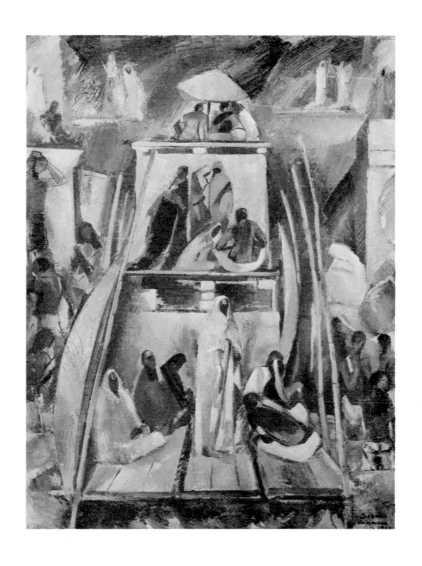

Maurice Sterne, NA
Benares. Oil
The Phillips Collection, Washington, D.C.

EUGENE SPEICHER (1883–1962)
(ANA 1912, NA 1925)
Katharine Cornell. 83¾ × 45½ inches.
Signed Eugene Speicher.
Albright-Knox Art Gallery, Buffalo, New York.
Gift of Julia R. and Estelle L. Foundation.

Speicher was a painter whose name in his lifetime almost seemed to be a synonym for success. Starting out in his native city of Buffalo, New York, as a young man with as much skill in athletics, especially basketball, as in art, he studied evenings at the Buffalo Art School from 1902–1906 seriously enough to win the Albright Scholarship and go to New York to study at the Art Students' League under W. M. Chase and others. Speicher's principal influence as a student, however, was Robert Henri in the latter's own school where fellow students were Bellows, Hopper, and DuBois. After a year of travel in Europe he began in 1912 to win the first of a seemingly endless succession of awards, the Proctor Prize at the National Academy. Two years later he won the Academy's Third Hallgarten Prize, the following year the Second Hallgarten Prize. The Beck Gold Medal from the Pennsylvania Academy and Third and Second Prizes at Pittsburgh's Carnegie Institute were added to his collection by 1923. Speicher subsequently reduced his portrait commissions to six a year to enable him to spend more time on the landscape and studio figure paintings. A diligent student of structure and design he produced some of the most solidly constructed figure paintings of his era. His paintings are owned by most of the prominent museums of the country.
Exhibited NAD 1910–15, 1918, 1925, 1939, 1944–45, 1947–48.

MAURICE STERNE (1878–1957)
(ANA 1935, NA 1944)
Benares. 40 × 30 inches. Signed, Sterne, Benares, 1912.
The Phillips Collection, Washington, D. C.

Sterne was born in Latvia and spent his youth in Moscow. After emigrating to the United States with his widowed mother in 1890, he sold newspapers and worked in a bronze foundry and a mirror factory as well as for a map engraver and as a bartender. All this time he was enrolled at Cooper Union and the National Academy, where he studied anatomy under Thomas Eakins. William M. Chase bought a painting from Sterne's first solo exhibit in 1902. The artist won the Mooney Traveling Scholarship at the National Academy in 1904 and promptly went to Europe. This was the beginning of an odyssey that carried Sterne around the world and attached to his name an exoticism which established his reputation as an artist. This was principally the result of his sojourn in Bali (1911–1914) where he produced several thousand drawings in oil on rice paper, the present painting deriving from that experience. After his Balinese years he returned to Italy where he had bought a forty-one room castle in Anticoli, near Rome, and developed a painting style fusing eastern and western sources. Sterne later turned to sculpture; "The Pilgrim Monument" in Worcester, Massachusetts is his most impressive work in this medium. The artist is represented in major American and European museums, including the Uffizi Gallery, Florence, which commissioned a self-portrait from him.
Exhibited NAD 1927, 1935–38, 1940–45, 1947–52, 1955–58.

Gilbert Stuart, HM(P)
Admiral Earl St. Vincent. Oil
Mr. and Mrs. Edward Benenson, New York

Walter Stuempfig, Jr., NA
Field Grass. Oil
National Academy of Design

GILBERT STUART (1755–1828) (HM(P) 1827)
Admiral Earl St. Vincent (1782). 30 × 25 inches.
Mr. and Mrs. Edward Benenson, New York.

Stuart was the son of a snuff mill owner in Newport, Rhode Island. His talent for drawing was
early recognized by an itinerant Scotch painter,
Cosmo Alexander, who arranged with his father
to take the young man back to Edinburgh as a
pupil. Alexander dropped dead in 1772, and Stuart
had to work his way back to America as a seaman.
Still with the aim of succeeding as an artist, Stuart
sailed from Boston in 1775 on the day before the
Battle of Bunker Hill. In London he worked as a
church organist and received help from Benjamin
West. Five years with the American master taught
Stuart how to paint faces, his self-proclaimed major virtue, and for a while he was the most popular
portraitist in London. Erratic in behavior, he was
usually only one step ahead of his creditors, until
he had the canny notion that the founders of the
new American Republic should have their faces
recorded by a painter with London-trained skills.
Beginning with his portraits of Washington,
Stuart has left us a legacy of probably the most
reliable likenesses of our Founding Fathers. He
never taught formally, but Mather Brown, John
Trumbull, John Neagle, and Samuel F. B. Morse
received instruction from him.
Exhibited NAD 1828.

WALTER STUEMPFIG, JR. (1914–1970)
(ANA 1951, NA 1953)
Field Grass. 25 × 30 inches. Signed, Stuempfig.
National Academy of Design.

Stuempfig was born in Germantown, Pennsylvania, educated at Germantown Academy, the
University of Pennsylvania (one year of architecture), and at the Pennsylvania Academy, where
he was awarded a Cresson Traveling Scholarship.
From 1949 until his death he was a member of the
Pennsylvania Academy. Frequent trips to Europe
provided him with the kind of aesthetic suste-
nance which he needed. Italy, in particular, was
his favorite place and the Italian Baroque period
his special time frame. At home he painted the
New Jersey beaches and portraits of family and
friends. Examples of his romantic realism can be
found in the Metropolitan Museum, the Museum
of Modern Art, the National Collection of Fine
Arts, the Philadelphia Museum, the Whitney Museum, and the Phillips Collection. He was awarded
the Benjamin Altman Landscape Prize at the National Academy, 1953, and the Corcoran Silver
Medal, 1947. His one man exhibitions were nearly
annual events and ranged from London to San
Francisco.
Exhibited NAD 1952–53, 1955–57, 1959, 1961–69.

Thomas Sully, HM(P)
Captain Jean T. David. Oil
The Cleveland Museum of Art

THOMAS SULLY (1783–1872) (HM(P) 1827)
Captain Jean T. David. 35¼ × 27¾ inches. Signed,
T S 1813.
The Cleveland Museum of Art.

Sully, the son of English actors, was born in Lin-
colnshire and came with them to this country in
1792. His parents placed him with an insurance
broker at the age of twelve, but he soon demonstrated that what he wanted to do was draw. He
first studied with his brother, a miniature painter,
and supported himself by miniatures for several
years. Sully moved to New York in 1806 to pur-
sue his career as a portrait painter, by this time in
oil. He met Gilbert Stuart and was even permitted
to observe the master's methods during a visit to
Boston. Because of an attractive offer from a patron he decided to live in Philadelphia, settling
there in 1808 and maintaining a residence for the
rest of his long life. A syndicate of seven patrons
sent Sully to England to paint and study, the pay-
ment to be a copy for each patron of an English
masterwork. In London he met West and Lawrence, the latter introducing him to many pro-
spective portrait sitters, including actress Fanny
Kemble, whom he painted several times. He
returned to Philadelphia in 1810 to become one
of the most sought after portraitists of the first
half of the 19th Century. Sully painted a version
of "Washington Crossing the Delaware" in 1818
(now in Boston), a portrait of Lafayette the same
year, 1824, that Morse painted Lafayette, and a
portrait of Queen Victoria the year of her acces-
sion, 1837, for the Society of the Sons of St.
George in Philadelphia.
Exhibited NAD 1827, 1830, 1832, 1834–35, 1839,
1843–44, 1852, 1864.

HENRY O. TANNER (1859–1937)
(ANA 1909, NA 1927)
The Miraculous Haul of Fishes. 38 × 47½ inches.
Signed, H. O. Tanner.
National Academy of Design. Exhibited 1927.

Tanner, America's first internationally renowned
Black artist, was born in Pittsburgh and moved
with his family to Philadelphia at the age of thirteen. There he determined to be an artist after
seeing a landscape painter at work in a public park.
At seventeen he left public school and went to
work for a flour merchant to please his father, a
minister who resisted his son's desire for art education. The art displayed in the Philadelphia Centennial Exposition of 1876 changed the father's
mind, and young Tanner was allowed to enroll in
the Pennsylvania Academy to study under Eakins.
Tanner went to Paris in 1891 and studied at Julian's
Academy with Benjamin Constant and J. P.
Laurens. After a brief visit home in 1892, he decided that Paris was his natural habitat. His
"Music Lesson" was accepted for hanging in the
Salon of 1894. After three other genre paintings
were hung the following year, Tanner shifted his
interest to religious painting and received an honorable mention with "Daniel in the Lions' Den"
in the Salon of 1896. "The Raising of Lazarus"
was such a success that he went to the Near East to
absorb the land of the Bible for future reference.
After another brief visit to the United States in
1903–04, Tanner returned to Paris to remain
there. He won silver medals at Buffalo in 1901,
St. Louis in 1904, and a gold medal at the Panama-Pacific Exposition in San Francisco, 1915.
Exhibited NAD 1885–87, 1909–10, 1925, 1929,
1934, 1938.

Henry O. Tanner, NA
The Miraculous Haul of Fishes. Oil
National Academy of Design

EDMUND C. TARBELL (1862–1938)
(ANA 1904, NA 1906)
Girl Reading. 32½ × 28½ inches. Signed, Tarbell.
Museum of Fine Arts, Boston.

Tarbell was born in West Groton, Massachusetts, raised in Boston, and was apprenticed as a lithographer's assistant in his youth. His art education began at the Museum of Fine Arts School, Boston, where he studied under Otto Grundman along with Frank Benson and Robert Reid. In 1883 Tarbell went to Paris with Benson where they both worked under Boulanger and Lefebvre at the Julian Academy. Tarbell returned in 1885 to Boston to begin a lifelong career as a portrait painter. Starting in 1889 he taught at the Boston Museum School for twenty-four years. Later he became principal of the Corcoran School, Washington, D. C. In 1890 Tarbell won the Clarke Prize and in 1894 the first Hallgarten Prize at the National Academy. He also won medals and awards in Chicago, Philadelphia, and Pittsburgh. While portrait painting formed the basis of his art life, he also did figure pieces, interiors, and still lifes. His aesthetic aims were summarized when he pointed to a sculpture by Rodin and said, "That is how I want to paint. Rodin just happened to paint in marble; but this is how I want to paint, with paint."
Exhibited NAD 1888–95, 1897, 1899, 1904, 1906, 1908, 1910, 1923–24, 1929.

ABBOTT H. THAYER (1849–1921)
(ANA 1898, NA 1901)
Winter Landscape. 29½ × 35½ inches. Signed.
National Academy of Design.

Thayer was born in Boston and spent his youth in Keene, New Hampshire, where his father was a physician. He early did a brisk business in portraits of friends' pets. He studied in Boston, then under J. B. Whittaker in Brooklyn and L. E. Wilmarth in New York City. In Paris he studied under Gérôme. In 1879 he opened a studio in New York, became president of the Society of American Artists, and for the next decade made the Hudson River region his adopted home. The mental illness and death of his wife by 1890 changed Thayer's whole outlook on life. He painted a succession of idealized, angelic women, one of which, in the Freer Collection, Washington, D. C., is dedicated to the memory of his dead wife. He received many awards—gold medals at the Pennsylvania Academy (1891), at Paris (1900), at the Pan-American Exposition, Buffalo (1901), and at the Carnegie International, Pittsburgh (1920) plus many other prizes. Thayer's lifelong interest in studying and painting animals led him to an analysis of animal protective coloration. From that he developed the theory of camouflage which was first published in 1897, then in science magazines, and finally in a book by his son in 1909. It became the basis for wartime camouflage in the First War. He spent his final years living at the foot of Mt. Monadnock, New Hampshire, painting the surrounding landscape.
Exhibited NAD 1867–75, 1877–78, 1880, 1894–95, 1898, 1908, 1915, 1921.

Louis C. Tiffany, NA
Duane Street, New York. Oil
The Brooklyn Museum

LOUIS C. TIFFANY (1848–1933)
(ANA 1871, NA 1880)
Duane Street, New York (1878). 27 × 30 inches.
Signed, Louis C. Tiffany.
The Brooklyn Museum.

Tiffany was the son of the founder of Tiffany and Co. in New York City whose formal education stopped at high school. He studied painting under George Inness and Samuel Colman in this country and Léon Bailly in Paris. His early interest in landscape gave way gradually to figure painting, and a youthful visit to the Near East aroused in him a love of color which he applied in his compositions. Tiffany was one of the secessionist artists who, along with LaFarge, Saint-Gaudens, et al., organized the Society of American Artists in 1877. By 1875 he had begun to experiment with stained glass and three years later established his first glass making factory. He invented a new method of making stained glass by forcing a pot metal glass into various shapes while the glass was in a molten state. By this means he was able to design within each glass area and form his windows according to his "mosaic" theory of construction. A huge window commission, weighing several tons, for the National Theater in Mexico City, provided him with a shopful of extra pieces which he converted into the ornamental glass products associated with his name. This Favrile glassware earned Tiffany many awards at international expositions between 1893 and 1926. He also designed a whole range of house furnishings. He established the L. C. Tiffany Foundation in 1919 to aid art students.
Exhibited NAD 1867–75, 1877–81, 1883, 1888–92, 1907–11, 1920–26, 1930–31.

GEORGE TWIBILL (1806–1836)
(ANA 1832, NA 1833)
Portrait of John Trumbull (1833). 26¾ × 19 inches.
National Academy of Design. Exhibited 1835.

Twibill was born in Lampeter, Lancaster County, Pennsylvania, and became the pupil and eventually the brother-in-law of Henry Inman. He was known primarily for his miniatures, but the present portrait of John Trumbull, painted the year before the artist's death, plus two other full length portraits of Trumbull and one of General Cummings attest to the young man's possible fame had he lived longer.
Exhibited NAD 1832–35.

JOHN VANDERLYN (1775–1852)
(Founder NA(Elect) 1826)
Portrait of Robert R. Livingston (1804).
45 × 34 inches.
The New York Historical Society.

Vanderlyn was born and raised in Kingston, New York. Following school at the age of sixteen he worked for a blacksmith and wagon painter. Vanderlyn's older brother, Nicholas, took him to New York and introduced him to print seller Thomas Barrow. He worked there for two years, studied drawing with Archibald Robinson, and returned to Kingston for a year to try painting portraits. Back in New York City he copied portraits by Gilbert Stuart, one of Aaron Burr. The latter was so impressed that he arranged for Vanderlyn to go to Philadelphia to study with the master for nine months. Burr then commissioned Vanderlyn to paint portraits of himself and his daughter and subsidized him for a five year stay in Paris, 1796–1801. In Rome Vanderlyn painted his first celebrated canvas, "Marius amid the Ruins of Carthage". In 1808 it received a gold medal at the Salon at the direction of Napoleon. In 1812 he painted his even more celebrated canvas, "Ariadne", the first American nude. When Vanderlyn returned home after the defeat of Napoleon, he fully expected to be greeted as a distinguished citizen. Instead his fortunes went into reverse, and for his remaining thirty-seven years he struggled against poverty. He painted many portraits (Monroe, Madison, Jackson, Z. Taylor, Calhoun, etc.) and some panoramas to raise money, but he died in his home town, an embittered, impoverished man.
Exhibited NAD 1830, 1832, 1839, 1844, 1851.

ELIHU VEDDER (1836–1923)
(ANA 1863, NA 1865)
Jane Jackson, Formerly a Slave. 18 × 18 inches.
Signed, 18V65.
National Academy of Design.
Exhibited NAD 1869.

Vedder was born in New York City, but spent his youth in Schenectady, with occasional trips to Cuba with his father. He began to study art at the age of twelve independently, then under T. H. Harrison of Sherburne, New York. Vedder went to Paris in 1856 and studied under F. E. Picot for one winter. This was followed by four years in Florence, Italy. He returned to New York, penniless, at the beginning of the Civil War. It was impossible to sell his paintings, so he resorted to commercial art, comic valentines, sketches for *Vanity Fair*, and calisthenic diagrams of dumbbell exercises. At the end of his New York stay he painted "Jane Jackson" and exhibited a drawing of the subject the same year, 1865, at the National Academy. At the conclusion of the war Vedder left the United States for his remaining fifty-eight years, except for occasional visits to arrange exhibitions and execute commissions. His main studio was in Rome but he also owned a villa on the Island of Capri. In 1884 he published a series of over fifty illustrations for *The Rubáiyát of Omar Kháyyam*, his major opus. They were exhibited in Boston in 1887 along with sixteen paintings in his abstracted, idealized figurative style, involved with the Soul, Death, Fate, Doubt, Faith, etc.
Exhibited NAD 1862–67, 1869–72, 1874, 1876, 1882, 1891.

Samuel Waldo, NA
William Jewett, NA
Portrait of Stephen Allen, Mayor of New York. Oil
Hirschl and Adler Galleries, New York

SAMUEL WALDO (1783–1861)
(Founder NA 1826, Joint ANA w. Jewett 1847)
WILLIAM JEWETT (1795–1874)
(Founder NA, 1826, Joint ANA w. Waldo 1847)
Portrait of Stephen Allen, Mayor of New York.
Oil on panel, 33 × 25¾ inches.
Hirschl and Adler Galleries, New York.

Waldo was born at Windham, Connecticut, into an old Yankee family. At sixteen he went to Hartford to receive some indifferent instruction in drawing. He sold a painting for fifteen dollars and rented a studio in Hartford. The expected customers did not appear, so Waldo painted signs to survive. He painted some portraits in Litchfield and met John Rutledge of South Carolina who invited him to go to that state to paint commissioned portraits. Waldo's three years in Charleston were successful enough to afford a trip to England. Letters of introduction to West and Copley eased his way, but in 1809 he returned to this country and settled in New York. Beginning in 1820 he formed a partnership with his student, William Jewett, to paint portraits as a team. Waldo continued to paint entire portraits himself which were generally superior to his partnership productions. Examples of his (self-portrait) and their (Andrew Jackson) collaboration can be found in the Metropolitan Museum. The Corcoran Gallery, Washington, D. C., the City Art Museum, St. Louis, and the New York Historical Society also own works. In particular New York's City Hall has portraits of several mayors by them.
Exhibited NAD 1844, 1861 (jointly with William Jewett 1826–31, 1845–49, 1851–52).

Jewett was born in East Haddam, Connecticut, and worked on his grandfather's farm until sixteen. He then apprenticed as a paint mixer for a coachmaker in New London. Some decorating gave him a taste for painting as a profession. Samuel Waldo discovered Jewett as a young man of talent and invited him to come to New York to study. This caused much acrimony between Jewett and his employer. The apprentice finally had to agree to pay the coachmaker for lost services plus interest before he could be released from his obligation. After three years of study with Waldo he began to assist the master in the studio. He also went to the Bowling Green customs house to draw from the imported plaster casts stored there. The two men made frequent painting excursions up the Hudson River. By 1817 Jewett was able to pay off the coachmaker, and three years later entered into full partnership with Waldo in the painting of portraits. Waldo did the heads and hands and Jewett painted the rest. This arrangement lasted for thirty-four years. The New York Historical Society, The Metropolitan Museum, and New York City Hall have many examples of their joint work.
Exhibited NAD (jointly with Waldo) 1826–31, 1845–49, 1851–52.

FRANKLIN WATKINS (1894–1972)
(ANA 1951, NA 1957)
Soliloquy (1932). 25¼ × 30¼ inches.
Signed, Watkins.
Whitney Museum of American Art,
New York.

Watkins was a native New Yorker who spent his boyhood in Philadelphia. The Groton School, the University of Virginia and the University of Pennsylvania provided schooling before he enrolled in the Pennsylvania Academy. Most of the remaining years of his life were spent at the Academy, first as a student and then as one of its most admired teachers. In 1931 Watkins burst upon the art scene when he won the Carnegie International first award for painting with his "Suicide in Costume", a dead clown with a smoking pistol in his hand. Watkins's painting style featured an introspective view of whatever subject he approached, whether it was his symbolic still lifes, figure paintings, or the four or five portraits he consented to undertake each year. In 1956 his portrait of Philadelphia's mayor, Joseph S. Clark raised the hackles of local authorities as being too brooding and poetic and nearly was not hung in city hall. The Museum of Modern Art, New York, gave him a retrospective exhibition in 1950. New York critics were hostile, and Watkins never again showed in New York. As an art juror in many exhibitions he was known as having wide ranging tastes and was generous to all phases of art. Of his own work he once said, "Great paintings bear the stamp of their time. I'm not sure that mine do."
Exhibited NAD 1927.

HARRY W. WATROUS (1857–1940)
(ANA 1894, NA 1895, PNA 1933–34)
Records. 15 × 11 inches.
Mr. and Mrs. George J. Arden, New York.

Watrous was a native of San Francisco, California, whose early schooling aroused a desire for an art education. He went to Paris in 1881 to study under Boulanger and Lefebvre at the Julian Academy and in Bonnat's atelier. His work in painting progressed so rapidly that a Parisian art dealer took on his work and began to sell it in London, the story-telling content of his highly polished small figure pieces appealing to collectors of that period. The Americans John D. Archbold, Benjamin Altman, W. C. Whitney, and J. S. Isidor were among those who bought Watrous paintings. As a consequence his reputation preceded him by the time he returned to the United States from Paris. In 1894 he won the Clarke Prize at the National Academy, in 1901 a bronze medal at the Pan-American Exposition, Buffalo, and in 1904 he was awarded a gold medal for the present painting, "Records". Watrous was a member of many artists' associations, and his work is widely distributed among the museums of the country.
Exhibited NAD 1886, 1889–91, 1894–1916, 1918–41.

Harry W. Watrous, PNA
Records. Oil
Mr. and Mrs. George J. Arden, New York

J. Alden Weir, PNA
Portrait of Mrs. J. A. Weir on Frank Duveneck's
Studio Balcony in Venice. Oil
Brigham Young University, Art Gallery, Provo, Utah

J. ALDEN WEIR (1852–1919)
(ANA 1885, NA 1886, PNA 1915–17)
Portrait of Mrs. J. A. Weir on Frank Duveneck's Studio Balcony in Venice (1883). 78 × 47 inches.
Brigham Young University, Art Gallery, Provo, Utah. Gift of Mrs. Mahonri Young.

Weir was the youngest of sixteen children of R. W. Weir, artist and art teacher at West Point Military Academy. Grant, Lee, Sherman, and Whistler were among his students. Young Weir was taught art by his father until, at eighteen, he enrolled at the National Academy school. In 1873 he embarked for Europe to study for the next four years. He first worked with Gérôme. In Paris he also met Whistler and Jules Bastien-Lepage. Bastien-Lepage introduced Weir not only to the ways of Paris and places in Holland and Spain, but also encouraged him to work directly from nature. After 1883 he had a studio at old 51 West Tenth Street and became associated with the first generation of American Impressionists: Hassam, Metcalf, Twachtman, etc. Weir helped to organize the Society of American Artists and the secessionist exhibiting group known as "Ten American Painters" in 1898. Even though he associated himself with local Impressionists, his painting has more kinship with the pictorial space of Japanese printmakers, Manet and Whistler. Always supportive of young artists and new ideas, he even encouraged the purpose behind the Armory Show of 1913. Typical work can be seen in the Metropolitan Museum, The Art Institute of Chicago, and in Washington.
Exhibited NAD 1875, 1877–82, 1884–92, 1894–96, 1898, 1901–11, 1914–15, 1917.

IRVING R. WILES (1861–1948)
(ANA 1889, NA 1897)
Tenth Street Studio. 34 × 46 inches. Signed, Irving Wiles.
M. Knoedler and Co., Ltd., New York.

Wiles was born in Utica, New York, and was educated at the Sedgwick Institute, Great Barrington, Massachusetts. His father taught him the rudiments of art, but he finally came to New York City to study under William M. Chase and then to Paris to study with Carolus-Duran and Lefebvre. Wiles's free dashing style was characteristic of his time, and he established himself as a portrait, landscape and genre painter in New York. He won the third Hallgarten prize at the National Academy, an honorable mention at the Paris salon, and several medals. He was one of eight painters commissioned by the National Art Committee to paint the history of the First World War. His portrait of William Jennings Bryan hangs in the State Department, Washington, D. C.
Exhibited NAD 1882, 1884–1921, 1925–28, 1930–36, 1939–45, 1947–48.

ALEXANDER H. WYANT (1836–1892)
(ANA 1868, NA 1869)
Moonlight and Frost. 28 × 36 inches.
The Brooklyn Museum.

Wyant was born in Evans Creek, Ohio, and was apprenticed to a harness maker at an early age. In 1857 he decided to become a painter. After consulting with George Inness in New York City, he sought and received the patronage of Nicholas Longworth of Cincinnati. This enabled him to study for a year at the National Academy and in 1865 in Düsseldorf. He then opened a studio in New York. In 1873 he suffered a stroke and was paralysed on his right side. This forced him to learn to paint with his left hand. His remaining years were spent shuttling between New York City in winter and Keene Valley and Arkville, New York, in summer. He concentrated almost exclusively on quiet landscapes of clearings in fields and woods.
Exhibited NAD 1865–92.

Sculpture

ROBERT I. AITKEN (1878–1949)
(ANA 1909, NA 1914)
The Flame. Bronze, 20 × 8 × 8 inches.
Signed, Aitken 1908.
National Academy of Design. Exhibited 1908
(Barnett Prize). Gift of Mrs. Robert I. Aitken.

Aitken was born in San Francisco and studied at
the Mark Hopkins Institute there. He started out
as a painter, but six months of study with an expatriate French sculptor convinced him to switch to
the three dimensional medium. He went to Paris
to continue his studies and returned to this country to become one of our best known portrait
sculptors. In 1908 he won the Barnett prize at the
Academy with the present piece. Aitken was represented in the Panama Pacific Exposition, San
Francisco, 1915, by four heroic figures, "Fire",
"Air", "Earth", and "Water", and a "Fountain of
Life". In San Francisco also is his monument to the
United States Navy and his sculpture of President
William McKinley. His statue of Frederic Rem-
ington was placed at the railroad station in New
Rochelle.
Exhibited NAD 1907–12, 1915, 1917, 1920–21,
1925, 1930, 1932, 1934.

JO DAVIDSON (1883–1952) (ANA 1944)
Gertrude Stein (1920).
Bronze, 31¼ × 23¼ × 24½ inches.
Whitney Museum of American Art, New York.

Davidson was born into a poor Russian family on
New York's lower East Side and early showed an
interest in drawing. At sixteen he won a scholarship to the Art Students' League. Davidson tried
studying medicine at Yale, but his discovery of
clay during a visit to the Yale School of Fine Arts
was too much for him. In New York he studied
with George DeForest Brush and sculptor Hermon McNeill. Then he went to the École des
Beaux-Arts in Paris. Davidson restricted himself
almost exclusively to portrait modeling throughout his career and became the most renowned and
sought after "facemaker" of his era. Heads of
state, military men, industrial magnates, literary
figures, and other public personalities felt that
only Jo Davidson could commit their features
satisfactorily to bronze. F. D. Roosevelt, Woodrow Wilson, Anatole France, Will Rogers,
George Bernard Shaw, John D. Rockefeller, and
Robert M. LaFollette were only a few of his many
subjects. Davidson's political views were strong.
He modeled busts of the Spanish Loyalist leaders,
1936–39. In 1942 he finished a memorial figure to
the victims of the Hitler atrocity at Lidice, Czech-
oslovakia. He also modeled busts of the founders
of the State of Israel.
Exhibited NAD 1907–08, 1927, 1934, 1945.

Jo Davidson, ANA
Gertrude Stein. Bronze
Whitney Museum of American Art, New York

DANIEL CHESTER FRENCH (1850–1931)
(ANA 1900, NA 1901)
Portrait Bust of Ralph Waldo Emerson. Bronze,
22 × 11 inches. Signed.
National Academy of Design.
Acquired 1902 Diploma Bust.

French was born in Exeter, New Hampshire, and
brought up in Concord, Massachusetts. After a
year at the Massachusetts Institute of Technology
he studied sculpture under J. Q. A. Ward and
anatomy under William Rimmer. French was
commissioned in 1873 by the towns of Concord
and Lexington to sculpt a figure to commemorate
the 100th anniversary of the "Shot Heard 'Round
the World" in 1875. The result was the famous
"Minute Man". At its unveiling French was in
Florence studying under Thomas Ball. Back in
this country he first set up a studio in Washington, D. C., 1876–78, and then had studios in Boston and Concord until 1887. After that year his
headquarters shifted to New York City, where he
remained. He was probably the best known American sculptor of his time because of his colossal con-
templative sculpture of Abraham Lincoln in the
Lincoln Memorial, Washington, D. C. French also
sculpted John Harvard for Harvard University,
historical busts for New York University's "Hall
of Fame", and figures of such prominent citizens
as U. S. Grant, Rufus Choate, General Hooker,
and Ralph Waldo Emerson. Emerson said of his
own bust, "That is the face I shave." French combined technical skill with a feeling of idealism
which suited his era.
Exhibited NAD 1879, 1888–90, 1901–02, 1908,
1910–11, 1914–15, 1918, 1920–21, 1925, 1930–31.

CHARLES A. GRAFLY (1862–1929)
(ANA 1902, NA 1905)
Bust of Paul Bartlett. Bronze, 16 × 8 × 9½ inches.
Signed, Grafly 1916.
National Academy of Design.
Exhibited 1917, gift of the
Whitney Museum of American Art, 1953.

Grafly was a native of Philadelphia and spent most
of his life in that city. After early schooling he became an apprentice in Struthers's stone monument shop where he "helped to carve countless
bits of sculpture on the Philadelphia City Hall."
He enrolled in the Pennsylvania Academy in 1884
and there studied anatomy under Eakins and
Anshutz. In 1888 he went to Paris to work under
Chapu at the Julian Academy and the following
year transferred to the École des Beaux-Arts for a
year. In 1890 he exhibited two heads in the Salon.
Grafly taught at the Pennsylvania Academy and
at Drexel Institute for many years. He won a
medal at the World's Columbian Exposition in
Chicago, 1893, and helped found the National
Sculpture Society. After another trip to Paris
in 1895 he returned to make Philadelphia his headquarters for the rest of his life. The only exceptions
were regular summer vacations to his summer
home in Gloucester, Massachusetts. Grafly's chief
accomplishment was in his portrait busts, especially of fellow artists Duveneck and Paxton. His
work is in New York University's Hall of Fame,
the Boston Museum of Fine Arts, and other major
collections.
Exhibited NAD 1906–10, 1912, 1915, 1917–18,
1925.

Daniel Chester French, NA
Ralph Waldo Emerson. Bronze
National Academy of Design

Charles A. Grafly, NA
Bust of Paul Bartlett, NA. Bronze
National Academy of Design

Herbert Haseltine, NA
Un Puyazo. Bronze
Whitney Museum of American Art, New York

HERBERT HASELTINE (1877–1962)
(ANA 1940, NA 1946)
Un Puyazo. Bronze, 21 × 22 inches. Signed on
base, Herbert Haseltine/(No. 2), 1912.
Whitney Museum of American Art, New York.

Haseltine was born in Rome but came to this
country for his education. After graduating from
Harvard in 1899, he studied art in Munich, Rome,
and Paris. During the First War he served as a
captain of Engineers in the AEF, helping organize
the camouflage section. Haseltine became a specialist in the sculpture of animals, mainly horses.
He not only modeled sleek winners, like his 3000-
pound statue of Man O' War in Lexington, Kentucky, of 1947, but also draught horses and the
war worn hulks of "Les Revenants", horses returning from battle. For thirteen years he worked
on a collection of sculptures of various animals for
the Field Museum in Chicago at the behest of
Marshall Field. In 1950 his statue of British Field
Marshal Sir John Greer Dill was unveiled by
President Harry S. Truman at Arlington National
Cemetery. Haseltine at one time sculpted a pair of
foot high horses' heads, cast in gold, bejeweled,
and mounted in rock crystal for Barbara Hutton.
One of his last important works was the equestrian statue of Washington in front of the National Cathedral, Washington, D. C. His cavalry
memorial, "The Empty Saddle", stands in the
Cavalry Club, London.
Exhibited NAD 1934, 1962.

MALVINA HOFFMAN (1887–1966)
(ANA 1925, NA 1931)
Bali Boy and Fighting Cock. Bronze,
37½ × 23 inches.
National Academy of Design. Acquired 1931.
Diploma Sculpture.

Hoffman was born in New York City and first
studied painting with J. W. Alexander. She
changed to sculpture and studied with Herbert
Adams and Gutzon Borglum in New York and
with Rodin in Paris. As a result of Rodin's in-
sistence on a bold naturalism, Hoffman's best
work evolved in her portraiture. She modeled her
own hall-of-fame of notables which included
Paderewski, Pavlova, Wendell Willkie, and
Katharine Cornell. Her "Bacchanale Russe",
1917, brought her international fame. Hoffman's
best known work was her anthropological series
done for Chicago's Field Museum. Begun in 1930,
"The Races of Man" occupied her for many years.
It consisted of anatomically accurate representa-
tions of people from Africa, Asia, Europe, the
Pacific Islands and North America. Among many
honors which she received was the French Legion
of Honor.
Exhibited NAD 1909, 1911–13, 1915–17, 1919–22,
1924, 1926, 1930, 1934, 1936, 1954–59, 1965, 1967.

CECIL HOWARD (1888–1956)
(ANA 1944, NA 1948)
Leaning Figure (c. 1929). 31 inches high, bronze.
Signed on base, Howard.
Whitney Museum of American Art, New York.

Howard was born in Clifton, Canada, but the family moved to Buffalo when he was two. At the age of thirteen he started clay modeling at the Art Students' League under James E. Fraser. In his later teens he went with his mother to Paris and stayed there for thirty-five years. Gradually his sculpture began to be shown at the Salon, and he kept himself alive by doing publicity, fashion drawing, and teaching the Argentine tango. Howard worked in a British hospital unit, 1914–18. He had a solo show at the Whitney Studio Club in the early 'Twenties, at this time carving marble and limestone. At the outbreak of the Second World War Howard drove a truck for the Red Cross carrying food and medicine to German prison camps. In 1943 he was recruited by the OSS to do secret work in Washington and London where his knowledge of French proved helpful. In 1947 the French Government purchased a stone nude and made him a Chevalier of the Legion of Honor. He won the Widener Medal, 1944, the Grand Prix for stone and the Grand Prix for bronze, both in 1937. His work is in the collections of the Whitney Museum, the Albright-Knox Art Gallery, Buffalo, and the Musée National d'Art Moderne, Paris. He was a member of the National Institute of Arts and Letters and the Société National des Beaux-Arts. Exhibited NAD 1916, 1920, 1927, 1944–45, 1949, 1957.

ANNA HYATT HUNTINGTON (1876–1973)
(ANA 1916, NA 1922)
Diana. Bronze, 99 × 36 inches.
National Academy of Design.
Gift from the artist, 1948.

Huntington was born in Cambridge, Massachusetts, the daughter of a college professor. She first studied art with Henry Kitson in Boston and then, 1905–06, at the Art Students' League under Hermon McNeill. She worked for a period with Gutzon Borglum. In 1915 she finished the bronze-equestrian sculpture of Joan of Arc in Riverside Park, New York. Another equestrian figure, "Cid Campeador" is in Seville. Busily productive during her long life, her work is located in more than 200 museums and galleries in the United States and abroad. Her 1965 statue of the Cuban patriot, José Marti, stands on Central Park South. Late in her career she had her sculptures cast in aluminum because of its "vibrant quality," her Lincoln equestrian figure being one of these. Huntington's last major work was a bronze, her equestrian sculpture of General Israel Putnam of 1969, which stands on her estate in Connecticut. She was an officer of the French Legion of Honor and a vice-president and trustee of the Hispanic Society, founded by her husband, Archer M. Huntington.
Exhibited NAD 1908–09, 1911–12, 1919, 1925, 1928, 1930, 1935–39, 1942, 1944, 1948, 1950–53, 1955, 1958, 1960, 1974.

Anna Hyatt Huntington, NA
Diana. Bronze
National Academy of Design

LEE LAWRIE (1877–1963) (ANA 1927, NA 1932)
The Sower (1928). Bronze, 21 × 12½ inches.
National Academy of Design. Study for figure
on Nebraska State Capitol—exhibited 1963;
acquired 1933. Diploma.

Lawrie was born in Rixdorf, Germany, and was
brought to this country as an infant. He attended
public schools in Illinois and Maryland and began
to work in the studio of sculptor Richard H. Park
in Chicago at the age of fourteen. In 1894 he went
to New York to study in the studios of Saint-
Gaudens and Philip Martiny. His first commission, in 1900, was for a set of reliefs in the Paw-
tucket, Rhode Island, Public Library. He designed
two equestrian groups for the St. Louis World's
Fair, 1904. From 1908–19 he taught at the Yale
School of Fine Arts, and simultaneously, 1910–12,
at Harvard University. From 1908–11 he sculpted
nine epic heroes for the U.S. Military Academy, at
West Point. Lawrie is best known for his sculpture
of "The Sower" (for which the present piece was
a study) and other works for the Nebraska State
Capitol, "Atlas" and other reliefs, for Rockefeller
Center, and for sculptures on the main entrance of
the Louisiana State Capitol, Baton Rouge. He was
a member of the American Academy of Arts and
Letters, the National Commission of Fine Arts,
the National Sculpture Society, the Architectural
League, and was a Fellow of the Royal Society of
Arts, London. He won medals from the American
Institute of Architects, 1921 and 1927, the Archi-
tectural League, 1931 and 1954, and from the
National Sculpture Society, 1951 and 1954.
Exhibited NAD 1963.

FREDERICK MACMONNIES (1865–1937)
(ANA 1901, NA 1906)
Bacchante with Infant Faun. (Cast in 1901 from the
1893 original.) Bronze, 85 × 25 × 31 inches.
Signed, F MacMonnies/1893.
Museum of Fine Arts, Boston.

MacMonnies was born in Brooklyn. His young
ambition to become a sculptor had its first realiza-
tion when Saint-Gaudens took him on as an assistant at the age of sixteen. During the master's
absence on one occasion MacMonnies did some
small clay studies and a copy of a Donatello bas-
relief. This work impressed Saint-Gaudens sufficiently that he assigned MacMonnies certain
sculptured tasks. He took evening classes at the
National Academy and the Art Students' League
and met many important artists, architects, and
clients in the Saint-Gaudens studio. In 1885 Mac-
Monnies went to Paris to study under Alexandre
Farguière and shortly became this sculptor's assistant. MacMonnies's earliest success was his
"Nathan Hale" for New York's City Hall Park
which earned him a medal at the Paris Salon of
1891. The event which catapulted him to fame
was his commission to sculpt a fountain for the
Chicago World's Fair of 1893. At the turn of the
century his weakened health forced him to turn
to painting, with which he had only moderate
success. He resumed sculpting in 1905, but in
those few years fashion had changed. Never again
did he have the same success. Perhaps his most
famous work was his "Bacchante with Infant
Faun" which was done in 1894 for the Boston
Public Library but was rejected as being too frank
in its nudity.
Exhibited NAD 1895, 1925, 1938.

Frederick MacMonnies, NA
Bacchante with Infant Faun. Bronze
Museum of Fine Arts, Boston

Paul Manship, NA
Flight of Night. Bronze
The Toledo Museum of Art

PAUL MANSHIP (1885–1966)
(ANA 1914, NA 1916)
Flight of Night. Bronze, 37 inches high.
Signed, Paul Manship/© 1916.
The Toledo Museum of Art.

Manship was born and raised in St. Paul, Minnesota. He attended the St. Paul School of Art evening classes in drawing and then went to Philadelphia to study sculpture under Charles Grafly at the Pennsylvania Academy. There he won a Rome Prize in 1909. Manship's three years in Rome were crucial to his development. Not only did he refine his considerable skill, but he also acquired a thorough taste for classical forms. Manship became one of the most adept bronze sculptors of his time, although he frequently accepted stone carving commissions. Among these latter are portraits of John Barrymore and John D. Rockefeller (both from 1918) and part of the American Military Cemetery at Anzio, Italy, in granite, 1952–55. Manship's most renowned sculpture is the 1934 gilded bronze fountain, "Prometheus", at Rockefeller Center, New York. His work can be seen in some three dozen American cities and in Europe. One example of the latter is his bronze celestial sphere for the Woodrow Wilson Memorial at the League of Nations, Geneva, Switzerland.
Exhibited NAD 1913–14, 1917, 1928, 1935 1939, 1944–45, 1955, 1963, 1966.

IVAN MEŠTROVIĆ (1883–1962)
(ANA 1948, NA 1956)
My Mother. (1926 copy of 1908 original.)
Marble, 42 × 37½ inches; base 22½ × 37½ inches.
Signed, Meštrović.
The Art Institute of Chicago.

Meštrović was the son of a village carpenter in Vrpolje, Croatia. As a boy he worked as a shepherd in the Dalmatian mountain village of Otavitze and with his father's encouragement carved small figures in wood and stone. At the age of fifteen he was apprenticed to a master mason in Split. Friends there aided him to study in Vienna where he gained entrance to the Art Academy only through his persistence. At the age of twenty-one he had a one-man show in Belgrade, the following year, one in Zagreb. In 1907 he set up shop in Paris where he met Bourdelle, Rodin, and Maillol. The four years prior to the First War he lived, worked, and studied archaic Greek sculpture in Rome. For the duration of the war Meštrović lived in Switzerland, after which, in 1922, he returned to Zagreb to become the director of the School of Fine Arts. Interest in his work in the United States resulted in an exhibition of his work at the Brooklyn Museum in 1924 and later in a 1947 exhibition at the Metropolitan Museum. He spent the rest of his years teaching in this country at Syracuse University and at the University of Notre Dame, becoming a United States citizen in 1954. Relief sculpture was his specialty, which can be seen in his war memorials and many museum acquisitions.
Exhibited NAD 1949.

Ivan Meštrović, NA
My Mother. Marble
The Art Institute of Chicago

Carl Milles, NA
Sun Glitter. Bronze
Worcester Art Museum, Worcester, Massachusetts

CARL MILLES (1875–1955)
(ANA 1948, NA(Elect) 1953)
Sun Glitter. Bronze, 31½ × 27 inches.
Signed, Carl Milles, c. 1917–18.
Worcester Art Museum,
Worcester, Massachusetts. Gift of
Mrs. Aldus Chapin Higgins.

Milles was born in Lagga, Sweden, and received his first sculpture instruction prior to 1898 at the Technical School, Stockholm. The following two years he studied at the École des Beaux-Arts, Paris, where he also worked in Rodin's atelier for several months. In 1900 Milles received two prizes in Paris, and these launched him onto a busy career as Sweden's foremost sculptor. He became professor of modeling at the Royal Academy of Art, Stockholm, but his highly personal style ran counter to prevailing Swedish preferences. He accepted a sculpture teaching position at Cranbrook Academy, Michigan, in 1929, and became a United States citizen in 1945. Perhaps his best known work is "The Meeting of the Waters" in St. Louis, Missouri, a large group of mythological figures celebrating the juncture of the Missouri and Mississippi Rivers. Milles executed over a hundred major works, mostly bronze, for gardens, public buildings, and parks in the United States and Europe. He received many honors, including the French Legion of Honor plus honorary doctorates from American and European universities.

AUGUSTUS SAINT-GAUDENS (1848–1907)
(ANA 1888, NA 1889)
Diana. Bronze, gilded. Height 112 inches.
The Metropolitan Museum of Art,
Rogers Fund, 1927, New York.

Saint-Gaudens was a native of Dublin, Ireland, who was brought in his infancy to this country, where his cobbler father set up shop in New York City. At the age of thirteen Saint-Gaudens was apprenticed to a cameo cutter and studied nights at Cooper Union (1861–65) and the National Academy (1865–66). The following year he went to Paris to study at the École des Beaux-Arts. There he continued to support himself with cameo cutting and copying antique sculptures on commission. He also carved his own first important work, the marble "Hiawatha". Back in the United States he established good personal and professional relationships with several leading American artists, notably H. H. Richardson, Stanford White, Charles McKim, and John La-Farge. Saint-Gaudens's "Admiral Farragut" in Madison Square, New York, has a base designed by White. With LaFarge he did two caryatids for Cornelius Vanderbilt's fireplace. His standing "Lincoln" in Lincoln Park, Chicago, and "The Puritan" in Springfield, Massachusetts, are two other superior works by Saint-Gaudens. His best known sculpture, however, is the bronze figure for the Adams Memorial in Rock Creek Cemetery, Washington, D.C. He also sculpted the equestrian figure of General Sherman in Central Park, New York. In addition Saint-Gaudens designed many medals and the 1907 $10 and $20 gold pieces.
Exhibited NAD 1875, 1888–89.

Augustus Saint-Gaudens, NA
Diana. Bronze, gilded
Rogers Fund, 1927
The Metropolitan Museum of Art, New York

Erwin F. Springweiler, NA
Razorbacks. Bronze
National Academy of Design

ERWIN F. SPRINGWEILER (1896–1968)
(ANA 1947, NA 1967)
Razorbacks. Bronze, 9 × 12 inches (including base).
National Academy of Design.
Acquired 1967, Diploma.

Springweiler was a native of Pforzheim, Germany, and first studied art there at the Art Craft School. He then attended the Munich Academy of Fine Arts and, after emigrating to the United States, assisted Paul Manship and Herbert Haseltine. It was perhaps his association with the latter sculptor that convinced him to concentrate on animal themes. He began to win awards in 1937 at the National Sculpture Society, and followed this with prizes from the National Academy, the Architectural League and the National Arts Club. Springweiler designed Congressional medals of George M. Cohan and General William L. Mitchell. His sculptures of animals are located at the Washington Zoo, Detroit, Michigan, and the Brookgreen Gardens. He was a member of the National Institute of Arts and Letters.
Exhibited NAD 1937–38, 1940–41, 1944–45, 1947–52, 1955–61, 1964–65, 1966.

LAUNT THOMPSON (1833–1894)
(ANA 1859, NA 1862)
Bust of Samuel F. B. Morse. Marble, 23 × 17 inches.
National Academy of Design. Exhibited 1870.

Thompson was born in Queens County, Ireland, and came to this country with his widowed mother at the age of fourteen. In Albany young Thompson found work as a handy man for Dr. James H. Armsby. E. D. Palmer had sculpted a bust of Dr. Armsby, and Thompson's interest in drawing provided the reason for his being accepted by Palmer as a studio boy. Thompson stayed with Palmer nine years and developed superior skills in modeling and carving. At the age of twenty-four he opened a studio in New York City at 51 West Tenth Street and began to build a custom in medallions and portrait busts. A colossal sculpture of Napoleon by Thompson was shown in the 1867 Paris Exposition. In 1875 he went to Italy for six years, after which he returned to the United States. A Thompson bronze of General Winfield Scott is at the Old Soldiers' Home, Washington, D. C. A bronze equestrian sculpture of General Burnside is in Providence, Rhode Island.
Exhibited NAD 1859–60, 1862–63, 1874, 1882.

JOHN Q. A. WARD (1830–1910)
(ANA 1862, NA 1863)
Freedman. Bronze, 19½ × 15 inches.
Signed, 1863.
National Academy of Design.
Exhibited NAD 1867. Presented to NAD to
replace bust of H. P. Gray.

Ward was born near Urbana, Ohio, and lived a
childhood of fishing, hunting, horseback riding,
and modeling clay people and animals in the
shop of the village potter. At the age of nineteen
he visited his sister in Brooklyn and persuaded
sculptor Henry Kirke Brown he would make a
good studio assistant. Ward remained with Brown
for seven years and even inscribed his name,
"J. Q. A. Ward, Asst." in the base of Brown's
1854 equestrian statue of Washington. "I spent
more time inside that horse than Jonah did inside
the whale", he later said. Two winters in Washington, D. C., produced several portrait busts of
political figures. In 1861 he began to design small
metal objects such as sword hilts, cane handles,
table bells, and pistol mountings. The New York
studio he moved into that year remained his headquarters for a succeeding half-century. In it were
executed "The Indian Hunter" of 1868, one of
Central Park's earliest and best sculptures; "Washington" of 1883, located on the steps of the Sub-
treasury Building; and the pediment of the Stock
Exchange. His "Henry Ward Beecher" is in front
of Borough Hall, Brooklyn. Ward traveled in
Europe but never studied there.
Exhibited NAD 1862–63, 1867–68, 1874, 1896.

OLIN L. WARNER (1844–1896)
(ANA 1888, NA 1889)
Portrait Bust of J. Alden Weir. Bronze,
22½ × 10½ × 7½ inches. Signed, Warner 1880.
Corcoran Gallery of Art, Washington, D. C.
Exhibited 1888.

Warner was a native of Suffield, Connecticut,
moved with his family to Amsterdam, New York,
and then to Brandon, Vermont. He was then
seventeen and drew and carved in chalk. He
learned telegraphy and supported himself by that
means in Albion and Rochester, New York, and
in Augusta, Georgia, until he had enough money
to study art. In 1869 he went to Paris and enrolled
in the École des Beaux-Arts to work under Jouf-
froy. The Second Empire fell, the Republic was
declared, and Warner joined the Foreign Legion
in protest against the Commune. Back home in
1872, he met with four years of discouragement.
He designed for a silver manufacturing company
and for a maker of bronze gas fixtures. A portrait
bust of art dealer Daniel Cottier turned the tide.
He began to do busts of many prominent people
and fellow artists. During the 1880's he also turned
out many neo-classical figures and reliefs. During
a trip west in 1889–91 Warner modeled terra
cotta portrait heads of many of the important
Indian chiefs of the Great Plains, including Chief
Joseph of the Nez Percés. His last five years were
spent sculpting commissions for the Connecticut
and Massachusetts state houses and bronze doors
for the Library of Congress. This last commission
was interrupted by his death in a bicycle accident
and was finished by Herbert Adams.
Exhibited NAD 1873, 1875–76, 1878–82, 1887–91,
1897.

Olin L. Warner, NA
Portrait Bust of J. Alden Weir, NA. Bronze
The Corcoran Gallery of Art

Sidney Waugh, NA
Zodiac Bowl. Engraved crystal
Steuben Glass, New York

SIDNEY WAUGH (1904–1963)
(ANA 1936, NA 1938)
Zodiac Bowl. Engraved crystal glass,
15½ × 15½ × 2⅛ inches. Dated 1937.
Steuben Glass, New York.

Waugh was born in Amherst, Massachusetts, attended the Massachusetts Institute of Technology, went briefly to Rome to study, and then to Paris, where he worked with Emilé Bourdelle and Henri Bouchard. During his three years with Bouchard he received the bronze medal of the Spring Salon, 1928, and its silver medal, 1929. That same year he won the Prix de Rome of the Rinehart School of Sculpture, Baltimore, and spent the next three years at the American Academy. After returning home he shortly became chief associate designer for Steuben Glass. It was in this capacity that his name became widely known, even though he continued to execute major sculpture commissions. Waugh did sculptures for the Buhl Planetarium, Pittsburgh, the Pulaski Monument, Philadelphia, the Bethlehem Steel Company, and the Bank of Manhattan. In Washington his principal works are groups at the National Archives, the Post Office Department and the Federal Reserve Board buildings, and a figure in the Attorney General's conference room. He was a member of the National Institute of Arts and Letters, the New York City Art Commission, and the Municipal Art Society. He held honorary degrees from Amherst College and the University of Massachusetts. Exhibited NAD 1939, 1947.

GERTRUDE VANDERBILT WHITNEY (1876–1942)
(ANA 1940)
Mother and Child (1935). Marble (Rosso Antico), 34 inches high. Signed, Gertrude V. Whitney. Whitney Museum of American Art, New York.

Whitney, the daughter of Cornelius Vanderbilt, was born and educated in New York. She began her sculpture career after marriage to Harry Payne Whitney. At the age of twenty-five she started studies with Hendrik C. Anderson, James Earle Fraser, and at the Art Students' League. She worked in Paris with Andrew O'Connor and briefly with Rodin. Whitney's first exhibited work was "Aspiration" in the 1901 Pan-American Exposition in Buffalo. In 1907 she opened a studio in Greenwich Village, and the following year won her first prize for "Pan" from the Architectural League. That same year she embarked on one of the most meaningful aspects of her career. From the exhibition "Eight American Painters" at the Macbeth Gallery she bought four paintings and began a collection that would eventually become the Whitney Museum of American Art. Whitney's sculpture continued with "Aztec Fountain" of the Pan-American Building, Washington, D. C., 1912, the Titanic Memorial at Potomac Park, Washington, D. C., 1914–31, and the "El Dorado Fountain" which won the bronze medal at the Panama Pacific Exposition, San Francisco, 1915. Her several war memorials in this country and France have an unsentimental directness unusual in such works. She received honorary degrees for her accomplishments as an artist and patron from New York University, 1922, Tufts University, 1924, Rutgers University, 1934, and Russell Sage College, 1940.
Exhibited NAD 1927.

Gertrude Vanderbilt Whitney, ANA
Mother and Child. Marble (Rosso Antico)
Whitney Museum of American Art, New York

Mahonri Young, NA
Boxers. Bronze
Hirschl and Adler Galleries, New York

WHEELER WILLIAMS (1897–1972)
(ANA 1938, NA 1940)
Primavera. Bronze, 8½ × 6 × 6 inches.
Signed, Wheeler Williams 1931.
National Academy of Design. Exhibited 1939.
Acquired 1940. Diploma.

Williams, a native of Chicago, was graduated *magna cum laude* from Yale, 1919, and received a Master of Architecture degree from Harvard, 1922. He then studied at the École des Beaux-Arts in Paris. Williams's sculpture won him honorable mention in the Prix de Rome competition, 1922, and in 1937 a gold medal at the Paris Exposition. The Michigan Avenue bridge in Chicago is decorated with his "Tablets to Pioneers". Fairmount Park, Philadelphia, displays his "Settlers of the Seaboard", the façade of the Parke-Bernet Galleries, New York, his "Venus of Manhattan", and the Children's Orthopedic Hospital, Seattle, his "Fountain of the Water Babies". Williams was president of the Fine Arts Federation of New York and of the National Sculpture Society. He was also a founder and president of the American Artists Professional League.
Exhibited NAD 1938–43, 1945, 1947–49, 1951–53, 1958, 1960, 1962–63, 1964, 1967.

MAHONRI YOUNG (1877–1957)
(ANA 1912, NA 1923)
Boxers. Bronze, 14 × 20½ × 8½ inches. Signed, Mahonri № 10 founder's mark: Roman Bronze Works.
Hirschl and Adler Galleries, New York.

Young was born in Salt Lake City, the grandson of Brigham Young. Native adobe was his first art material, but when Cyrus Dalling came to Salt Lake City to sculpt a statue of Brigham Young in 1897, he introduced the youth to clay. Two years later Young was enrolled in the Art Students' League. Then off to Paris, where he studied at the Julian, Colarossi, and Delacluse academies. In Utah in 1912 he executed a series of drawings of the Navaho Indians and a series of bronze reliefs, etchings and pastels documenting Navaho life. It was in New York, however, that he found the subject matter which ultimately meant most to him. His bronzes of boxers and laborers allied his work with the earlier "Ashcan" painters. He taught for many years at the Art Students' League, everything from printmaking and illustration to painting and sculpture. The Metropolitan Museum owns Young's "Man with a Pick" and "Stevedore" plus several watercolors; the Whitney Museum owns "Right to the Jaw". He was a member of the American Academy of Arts and Letters, the National Sculpture Society, and the Society of American Etchers.
Exhibited NAD 1908, 1910–16, 1920, 1923, 1925, 1930–34, 1936, 1938–41, 1944–45, 1955.

Graphic Art

John Taylor Arms, NA
Basilica of the Madeleine, Vézelay. Etching
National Academy of Design

JOHN TAYLOR ARMS (1887–1953)
(ANA 1930, NA 1933)
Basilica of the Madeleine, Vézelay. Etching,
12⅝ × 7¼ inches, 3rd State. Signed in plate,
J T Arms—in pencil John Taylor Arms, 1929.
National Academy of Design. Exhibited 1930.

Arms was born in Washington, D. C., and studied
at Princeton University and at the Massachusetts
Institute of Technology, where he earned bachelor's and master's degrees in science. A skilled
craftsman, Arms became one of the most admired
etchers of his day. Beginning in 1927 when he exhibited architectural etchings at the National Arts
Club and the Salmagundi Club, Arms showed his
work in principal exhibitions in the United States
and Europe. He is represented in the British and
Victoria and Albert Museums, London, the Toronto Art Gallery, the Metropolitan Museum, the
Philadelphia Mueseum of Fine Arts, the Detroit
Institute of Arts, the Boston, Fogg, Brooklyn,
and Seattle Museums, and The Art Institute of
Chicago. He was a member of principal art organizations including the National Institute of
Arts and Letters, and he authored several books on
prints and printmaking.
Exhibited NAD 1921–24, 1927–32, 1935–36, 1938–
42, 1944–54.

GEORGE BELLOWS (1882–1925)
(ANA 1909, NA 1913)
A Stag at Sharkey's (1917). Lithograph on cream
paper, No. 46. 18¾ × 23¾ inches. Signed,
Geo. Bellows.
The Brooklyn Museum.

(For biography see p. 29.)

GEORGE BELLOWS (1882–1925)
(ANA 1909, NA 1913)
Dance in a Madhouse (1907). Black and red crayon,
charcoal, ink and gouache. 18⅞ × 24⅝ inches.
Signed, Geo. Bellows.
The Art Institute of Chicago.

George Bellows, NA
Dance in a Madhouse. Black and red crayon,
charcoal, ink and gouache
The Art Institute of Chicago

FEDERICO CASTELLON (1914–1971)
(ANA 1947, NA 1963)
All Saints of Palma. Color lithograph, 11/35,
14½ × 21 inches. Signed, Castellon.
National Academy of Design.
Exhibited 1965.

Castellon was born in Almeria, Spain, and came
to this country at the age of seven. At eighteen he
painted a mural in Erasmus Hall High School,
Brooklyn, with the support of Diego Rivera. In
1934 he received a fellowship from the Spanish
government to study in his native country where
he remained for two years until the beginning of
the Revolution. Back in the United States he resumed his painting career and won The Art Institute of Chicago's Logan Prize in 1939. Castellon
became an American citizen in 1943 and taught
successively at Teachers' College of Columbia
University, Pratt Institute, and Queens College,
all in New York City. Castellon's brand of expressionism is represented in the Whitney Museum, the Philadelphia Museum, the Museum of
Modern Art, The Art Institute of Chicago, the
Library of Congress and other principal collections. He was a Guggenheim Fellow twice: in
1941 and in 1950. The second fellowship he used
for travel and work in Italy. He was a member
of the National Institute of Arts and Letters.
Exhibited NAD 1938, 1940–41, 1944–45, 1949,
1963–65.

FREDERICK CATHERWOOD (1799–1854)
(HM(P) 1837)
City of Quezeltenango. Sepia wash and pencil,
4¼ × 7 inches.
National Academy of Design.

Catherwood was born in London and received
elementary education in a nearby day school. At
the age of sixteen he was apprenticed to Michael
Meredith, architect, making drawings on topo-
graphical tours of England. In 1821 he went to
Rome, worked with the Duchess of Devonshire
in her Forum excavations and made his first ar-
cheological drawings in the Catacombs. In Sicily
he painted "Mount Etna from the Ruins of Taura-
mina", shown at the National Academy in 1839.
In 1823 he was in Egypt. The following year, with
Henry Parke and Joseph Scoles, he hired a vessel
and traveled up the Nile to record the clusters of
ruins in the Nubian country of the Upper Nile.
In 1833 Catherwood was off to the Sinai and Jerusalem. He dressed as a Turkish merchant and drew
ruins with the aid of the "camera lucida", which
assured their accuracy. He painted a panorama of
Jerusalem, later shown in New York, and at great
risk drew the interior of the Mosque of Omar in
the Dome of the Rock, the first infidel to do so.
Catherwood arrived in New York in 1836 and
worked here three years as architect, panoramist,
and lecturer. In 1839 he set out with John L.
Stephens on an expedition to Central America
where he became the first accurate draughtsman
of ancient Mayan remains. He returned to London
in 1852, and set sail for the United States in 1854
on the S. S. Arctic which sank in a collision in the
Atlantic.
Exhibited NAD 1839, 1843, 1845.

WILLIAM MERRITT CHASE (1849–1916)
(ANA 1888, NA 1890)
Footpath. Pastel, 23 × 14¾ inches. Signed, Wm. M. Chase, c. 1884–5.
Kenneth Lux, New York.

(For biography see p. 43.)

ASA CHEFFETZ (1896–1965)
(ANA 1938, NA 1944)
Monday, The American Scene. Wood Engraving, No. 21/75. 9½ × 13⅛ inches. Signed, Asa Cheffetz. Prints Division, The New York Public Library, Astor, Lenox and Tilden Foundations.
Exhibited 1934 at the NAD.

Cheffetz, born in Buffalo, studied art at the Boston Museum School and at the National Academy. His superior skills as an engraver have been widely recognized, beginning with his early showing at the National Academy. Cheffetz began winning awards at the Pennsylvania Academy in 1928 and followed at The Art Institute of Chicago, 1930, the Los Angeles Museum of Art, 1934, the Diploma of Honor, Warsaw, Poland, 1936, the Chicago World's Fair, 1934, and purchase prizes from the Library of Congress, 1943 and 1945. His work is represented in the Library of Congress, the Cleveland, Baltimore, Boston, and Metropolitan Museums, The Art Institute of Chicago, Carnegie Institute, and the State of Israel collection. Cheffetz designed the official bookplate for the Library of Congress.
Exhibited NAD 1920, 1935–36, 1938–41, 1944–49, 1951, 1954.

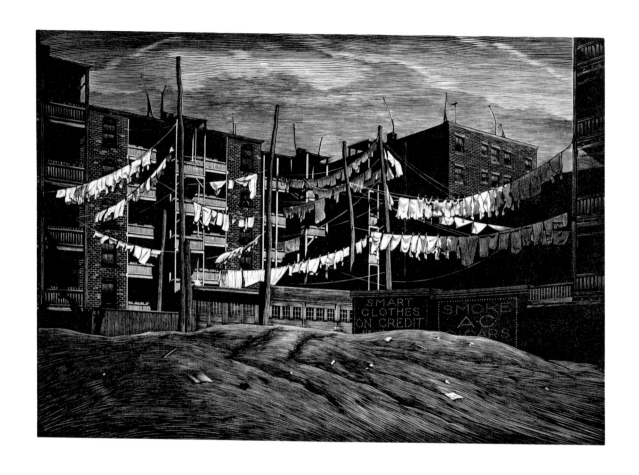

Asa Cheffetz, NA
Monday, The American Scene. Wood engraving
Prints Division, The New York Public Library,
Astor, Lenox and Tilden Foundations

166

TIMOTHY COLE (1852–1931)
(ANA 1906, NA 1908)
Coronation of the Virgin (after El Greco) (1930).
Wood Engraving, 8 × 8⅛ inches. Signed,
Timothy Cole.
The Brooklyn Museum.

Cole was born in London and brought to this
country at the age of five. After trying to build a
business as a hatter in New Jersey, Cole's father
moved to Chicago to try his fortune. Sixteen at
the time, Cole was apprenticed to a commercial
wood engraver. The Chicago fire shortened the
apprenticeship to three years. Cole went to New
York and promptly got work on *Frank Leslie's
Illustrated*, *Hearth and Home*, and *Scientific American*. He became one of the most sought after wood
engravers in the publishing industry. By the age
of thirty-one his skill in reproducing old master
paintings was such that he sailed for Europe in
search of more originals. He stayed for twenty-
seven years, and the work he sent back for reproduction in *Century Magazine* did much to create
that publication's reputation as an art magazine.
Cole returned to the United States at fifty-eight
to great acclaim but with only $750. His publish-
ers helped him to recoup by printing an album of
his work. He lived a chancy life of master of revels, a pioneer nudist, and a bon vivant. The introduction of photo engraving made him the last of
the great wood engravers. His last years were
made comfortable by patronage from the Wide-
ners and Sir William Van Horne. He was a member of the American Academy of Arts and Letters.
Exhibited NAD 1921, 1925, 1927, 1930–31.

MOSELEY I. DANFORTH (1800–1862)
(Founder NA 1826, HM(P) 1827)
The Sentry Box (after a painting by C. R. Leslie).
Mezzo-engraving, 14¼ × 10 inches. Dated 1833.
National Academy of Design.

Danforth was born in Hartford, Connecticut, received his early schooling there, and was apprenticed at the age of eighteen to Asaph Willard of
the Hartford Graphic and Bank Note Engraving
Company. After three years he moved to New
Haven to work as an engraver, then to New York
in 1825 for the same purpose. During three years
here he was active in the formation of the Academy, but left to continue his studies in London in
1827. There he stayed until 1840, at which time he
returned to New York and concentrated on bank
note engraving. An entrepreneur at heart, Danforth organized and headed seven bank note engraving companies with various partners and in
various cities. In 1858 he was one of the prime
movers in the important merger of bank note engraving companies into the American Bank Note
Engraving Company, of which he became vice
president. Engraving as an art was replaced in his
later years by watercolor painting and by his
copies from the Italian masters.
Exhibited NAD 1826, 1834.

ADOLF DEHN (1895–1968) (ANA 1942, NA 1961)
Die Walküre. Lithograph,
13⅜ × 17¾ inches. Signed, Adolf Dehn, 1930.
The Brooklyn Museum.

Dehn was born in Waterville, Minnesota, where his father was a commercial trapper and fisherman. After three years of study at the Minneapolis School of Fine Arts he received a scholarship to the Art Students' League, New York. He spent the following eight years during the 'Twenties in Vienna, Berlin, Paris, and London. Dehn's earliest reputation was as a satirical lithographer, a milder George Grosz, but in 1936 he gave up the print medium for watercolor for the next nine years. He then resumed lithography and added oil painting to his media. He won Guggenheim Fellowships 1939 and 1951 and traveled widely in Central America, Europe, Africa, Asia, and the Near East. In 1943 he won First Prize at the International Watercolor Exhibition at The Art Institute of Chicago. Dehn was a member of the National Institute of Arts and Letters, and his prints and paintings can be found in most of the public collections in the country.
Exhibited 1936, 1938, 1940–41, 1946, 1949, 1960, 1962–69.

KERR EBY (1889–1946) (ANA 1930, NA 1934)
The Caissons Go Rolling Along. Etching,
10⅛ × 14½ inches. Signed, Kerr Eby.
National Academy of Design.

Eby was born in Tokyo of Canadian missionary parents. He came to the United States in 1907 and studied at Pratt Institute and the Art Students' League. After doing early illustration he developed into an expert etcher. In the First War he was a sergeant in the Army Engineers, and his reactions to that experience he put into a series, "War", in 1935, Eby designing the set to be a modern equivalent of Goya's "Disasters of War". His reputation as an etcher was international, and his depictions of the combat realities of both World Wars are some of the angriest diatribes against war in this century. His series based on the landing of the Marines in Tarawa, in the Pacific, 1943–44, is particularly harrowing. Eby was a member of the National Institute of Arts and Letters and of several societies of etchers.
Exhibited NAD 1921–24, 1927–28, 1930–32, 1935, 1936, 1938–41, 1944–46.

CHARLES DANA GIBSON (1867–1944)
(ANA 1918, NA 1932)
From the Bartender's Standpoint. Pen and ink.
13 × 21¾ inches. Signed, C. D. Gibson.
National Academy of Design.

Gibson was born in Roxbury, Massachusetts, and
spent his youth in Flushing, New York. He studied with Saint-Gaudens briefly at the age of thirteen but returned to finish high school. He then
enrolled at the Art Students' League to work
under Cox, Chase, and Eakins. A strapping six-
footer, he was a sportsman who enjoyed rowing,
swimming, and weight lifting. In 1886 Gibson
sold his first drawing to the three-year-old
humor magazine, *Life,* and launched himself on
one of the most meteorically successful American
careers in illustration. He drew his breezy pen and
ink depictions of various American types for
many magazines: *Puck, Tid-Bits, Harper's, Scribner's,* and *Century* employed him to draw cartoon
comments on society and to illustrate stories. Gibson's friendship with Richard Harding Davis resulted in two collaborative books. The "Gibson
Girl" became the model for all young women and
is still synonymous with turn of the century style.
Tired of his fame, Gibson turned to oil painting,
particularly portraits; but first the panic of 1907
interrupted this effort and then changing fashion
ultimately passed him by. He was elected to the
American Academy of Arts and Letters in 1921.
An exhibition of 100 of his paintings at the National Academy in 1934 was well received by the
press.
Exhibited NAD 1930, 1939, 1944–45.

GORDON GRANT (1875–1962)
(ANA 1942, NA 1947)
Men with Oars. Etching, 10 × 8 inches. Signed,
Gordon Grant.
National Academy of Design.
Exhibited 1940. Acquired 1947.
One of six Diploma prints.

Grant was born in San Francisco of Scottish parents who sent the boy at the age of thirteen back to
Scotland for schooling. The four-month sail
around the tip of Cape Horn made a deep impres-
sion on the young man which influenced his
career. After school he studied art in the Heath-
erly and Lambeth Art Schools in London. Back in
San Francisco in 1895 Grant became a staff artist
for the *Examiner.* The following year he started in
the same capacity for the *New York World,* covering the Boer War for *Harper's Weekly.* Grant
also worked for *Puck* for eight years. The years
following 1920 were concentrated on painting,
etching, and lithography. The tremendous popularity of his work resulted from his vast authentic
knowledge of ships and the sea. His annual exhibitions were almost always sellouts, and his work
received many awards. Two of his paintings
were purchased by the National Academy for the
Henry Ward Ranger Fund. He is represented in
many major museums, and his work lives on in
his many illustrated books for both adults and
children.
Exhibited NAD 1920, 1922–23, 1929, 1931–35,
1938, 1940–41, 1944–45, 1947–49, 1951, 1953,
1955–56, 1963.

WILLIAM GLACKENS (1870–1938)
(ANA 1906, NA 1933)
Yuletide Revels (1910). Ink, pencil and watercolor
wash, 24½ × 18½ inches on illustration board
(A cover for *Collier's Magazine*). Signed,
W. Glackens.
The Brooklyn Museum.

(For biography see p. 64.)

GEORGE GROSZ (1893–1959) (ANA 1950)
Charwoman (1924). Pencil, 25⅝ × 20⅝ inches,
on tan paper. Signed, Grosz.
The Brooklyn Museum.

(For biography see p. 64.)

George Grosz, ANA
Charwoman. Pencil on tan paper
The Brooklyn Museum

CHILDE HASSAM (1859–1935)
(ANA 1902, NA 1906)
Washington's Birthday (1916). Etching, artist's proof—12⅞ × 7 inches. Signed with monogram. Prints Division, The New York Public Library, Astor, Lenox and Tilden Foundations.

(For biography see p. 69.)

(For biography see p. 69.)

ARTHUR W. HEINTZELMAN (1891–1965)
(ANA 1933, NA 1937)
Le Valaison. Etching, 11 × 14¼ inches.
National Academy of Design. Exhibited 1935.

Heintzelman was born in New Jersey and raised in Providence, Rhode Island. His early interest in drawing led him to an art education at the Rhode Island School of Design. Traveling fellowships for two years introduced him to the art of Europe. Upon his return he assumed the position of head of the Fine Arts Department of the Detroit School of Design and then became a faculty member and eventual head of the Drawing and Painting Department of the Rhode Island School of Design. An exhibition of his etchings in 1916 at Goodspeed's Book Shop in Boston was such a success that he concentrated on that medium from then on. He went to Paris, studied with Forain, and stayed there from 1921 to 1935. The Depression of the 'Thirties reduced the demand for his work. He sold his Swiss studio and returned to the United States. In 1941 he started another career as Keeper of Prints at the Boston Public Library and Curator of the Albert Wiggin Collection. He wrote and lectured extensively on the great printmakers, past and present. After his retirement he did much traveling and drew wherever he went. His work can be found in the country's principal print collections.
Exhibited NAD 1931, 1935–36, 1938–41, 1944–46, 1949, 1966.

ALFRED JONES (1819–1900)
(ANA 1844, NA 1851)
Sparking (after a painting by F. W. Edmonds).
Engraving, 13 × 17 inches. Dated, 1839.
National Academy of Design. Exhibited 1845.

Jones was a native of Liverpool, England, who emigrated to the United States as a young man and was apprenticed to Rawdon, Wright, Hatch and Edson, engravers in Albany, New York. While earning his living as an engraver for reproduction, he did original vignette engravings and also painted. In 1867 he executed a series of engravings illustrating the Canadian parliament in action in Ottawa for *Harper's Weekly*.
Exhibited NAD 1844–45, 1850, 1857–60, 1866, 1868–71.

JOHN LAFARGE (1835–1910)
(ANA 1863, NA 1869)
Angel Placing the Seal. (Design for the Watson window, Trinity Church, Buffalo.) Pencil on tracing paper, 16⅜ × 8 inches. Signed, LaFarge. The Brooklyn Museum.

(For biography see p. 86.)

PAUL LANDACRE (1893–1963)
(ANA 1939, NA 1946)
Growing Corn. Wood engraving,
8¾ × 4½ inches. Signed, Paul Landacre.
National Academy of Design. Exhibited 1940.

Landacre was born in Columbus, Ohio, and attended public school and Ohio State University
in his home town. A lifetime of concentration on
the art of wood engraving developed Landacre
into one of the most skilled printmakers in the
United States. For the two decades from 1933 to
1953 he won numerous awards from printmaking
organizations and the Library of Congress. His
work is owned by the Library of Congress, the
New York Public Library, the Metropolitan Museum of Art, the Boston Museum of Fine Arts, the
Museum of Modern Art, the Columbus, Ohio,
Public Library and the Victoria and Albert Museum, London, England. He illustrated many
books, five of which were included in the "Fifty
Books of the Year". He taught at the Otis Art
Institute, Los Angeles, and was a member of the
Society of American Graphic Artists.
Exhibited NAD 1936, 1938, 1940–41, 1943–45,
1949, 1955.

RICO LEBRUN (1900–1964)
(ANA 1962, NA 1963)
Lone, Great Mutilated Figure (Dante's *Inferno*,
Canto XXVIII). Ink wash, 39¹¹⁄₁₆ × 28 inches.
Signed, Lebrun, 1961.
Worcester Art Museum,
Worcester, Massachusetts.

Lebrun was a native of Naples, Italy, and was educated at the National Technical Institute and the
Naples Academy of Fine Arts. At the age of
twenty-two he became a designer and supervisor
in a stained glass factory. When the factory opened
a branch in Springfield, Illinois, Lebrun moved to
the United States. He made frequent return trips
to Italy to study the Renaissance and Baroque
masters who affected his mature style. Moving to
New York, he became a successful commercial
artist, won a Guggenheim Fellowship with a
mural project, taught at the Art Students' League,
then transferred to California in 1938. By this time
the Spanish Civil War and other European crises
caused Lebrun to shift his attention to more ex-
pressionistic methods and subject matter. He
taught at the Chouinard Art Institute in Los Angeles and instructed in animation at the Disney
Studio, "Bambi" being largely due to his efforts.
From 1944 to 1946 he was artist in residence at the
Santa Barbara Art Museum. Much of his painting
was monochromatic. A period in the mid-'Fifties
colorfully reflected a stay in Mexico, but his
Crucifixion series, the Buchenwald suite, the
series for Dante's *Inferno* and Brecht's *Threepenny
Opera* stress tone rather than color. Lebrun was
working on a series of thirty sculptures at his death.

Rico Lebrun, NA
Lone, Great Mutilated Figure
(Dante's Inferno, Canto XXVIII). Ink wash
Worcester Art Museum, Worcester, Massachusetts

Louis Lozowick, NA
Still Life No. 2. Lithograph
The Brooklyn Museum

LOUIS LOZOWICK (1892–1973)
(ANA 1971, NA 1972)
Still Life No. 2. Lithograph, 10¼ × 13¼ inches.
Signed, Louis Lozowick 1929.
The Brooklyn Museum.

Lozowick was born in Kiev, Russia, coming to
the United States at the age of fourteen. He studied art for three years at the National Academy
and then graduated from Ohio State University
just prior to joining the army in the First World
War. He first exhibited paintings, based on
sketches of American cities, in Berlin, 1923. He
returned to the United States in 1926 where he
resorted to commercial art to survive while cir-
culating his paintings in group exhibitions in museums and galleries. He became best known for
his lithographs of skyscrapers, constructions and
machinery, sixty-four of which, covering a span
of fifty years, were shown in a retrospective exhibition at the Whitney Museum in 1972. Lozowick
won many awards in Chicago, Philadelphia,
Cleveland, Brooklyn, Rochester, Dallas and else-
where. He is represented in the Whitney Museum, the Museum of Modern Art, the Library of
Congress, the New York Public Library, the
Metropolitan Museum, and in Boston, Cleveland,
Pittsburgh and the Victoria and Albert Museum,
London. He was a member of principal art organizations.
Exhibited NAD 1927–28, 1935–36, 1938, 1940–41,
1943–49, 1956, 1962–63, 1965, 1972–73.

REGINALD MARSH (1898–1954)
(ANA 1937, NA 1943)
Tattoo-Shave-Haircut. Etching, artist's proof—
9⅞ × 9⅞ inches. Signed, in pencil,
Reginald Marsh; also on plate, Marsh, 1932.
Prints Division, The New York Public Library,
Astor, Lenox and Tilden Foundations.

(For biography see p. 91.)

Reginald Marsh, NA
Tattoo-Shave-Haircut. Etching
Prints Division, The New York Public Library,
Astor, Lenox and Tilden Foundations

JEROME MYERS (1867–1940)
(ANA 1920, NA 1929)
Children Playing. Pencil, 8 × 10 inches. Signed,
Jerome Myers.
The Brooklyn Museum.

(For biography see p. 96.)

THOMAS W. NASON (1889–1971)
(ANA 1936, NA 1940)
On the Island. Wood engraving, 5¼ × 10 inches.
Signed, TW Nason, 1937.
National Academy of Design. Exhibited 1939.
Acquired 1941, Diploma.

Nason was born in Dracut, Massachusetts, and
was educated at Tufts University. Through the
years that followed he developed a quiet, per-
suasive oeuvre of wood engraving on simple architectural themes. From the time in 1929 when
he first won a prize at the Philadelphia Print Club,
his work was similarly honored at The Art Institute of Chicago, 1930, the City of Warsaw,
Poland, 1933, the Library of Congress, 1943 and
1945, and several times at the Society of American
Etchers. Nason's engravings are owned by the
New York and Boston Public Libraries, The Art
Institute of Chicago, the Baltimore, Cleveland,
and Boston Museums, the Victoria and Albert
Museum, London, and the Bibliothèque Nationale, Paris.
Exhibited NAD 1935–36, 1938–41, 1944–51, 1954,
1956, 1959.

Joseph Pennell, NA
The End of the Day, Gatun Lock. Lithograph on yellow paper
The Brooklyn Museum

JOSEPH PENNELL (1860–1926)
(ANA 1907, NA 1909)
The End of the Day, Gatun Lock (1912). Lithograph
on yellow paper, 17⅛ × 21⅝ inches. Signed,
Joseph Pennell.
The Brooklyn Museum.

Pennell was a native of Philadelphia who acquired
his basic art education at the Industrial School of
Art and at the Pennsylvania Academy. In addition
he was befriended by a local etcher, Gerome
Ferris, who invited him to visit his studio to learn
that craft. The lectures of Seymour Haden convinced him that Whistler was the greatest living
etcher, and Pennell's early work bears the Whistler mark. The two artists later became friends,
and Pennell and his wife published a biography of
Whistler in 1906. Pennell illustrated for *Scribner's*
and *Century* magazines and traveled widely for his
material. His travels can be traced accurately by
the titles of his pen and ink drawings from Philadelphia to Rome, from the Italian highways to
English roads, from the Hebrides to the Alps,
from the Thames to the Rhone. After 1908 he
began to depict industrial subjects rather than his
earlier romantic ones. Mills, stockyards, and construction, especially the building of the Panama
Canal, commanded his attention. Pennell said
that 1912 was the busiest year of his life. He was
then concentrating on lithography, and, besides
the Canal studies, drew San Francisco's Chinatown, Yosemite, the Grand Canyon, Washington, D. C., and the New York waterfront. He
was also one of the most popular teachers at the
Art Students' League.
Exhibited NAD 1908–12, 1914, 1920–25.

ERNEST D. ROTH (1879–1964)
(ANA 1920, NA 1928)
Florentine Palaces. Etching, 10 × 12 inches.
Signed and titled in plate, E. D. Roth—in
pencil Ernest D. Roth, 1927.
National Academy of Design. Acquired 1928
as one of six Diploma prints.

Roth was a painter and etcher of scenes in New
York, Italy and Spain. From 1915 to 1935 he won
many awards, and his work is owned by the Library of Congress, The Art Institute of Chicago
and other collections here and in Europe. Roth
became a member of the National Institute of
Arts and Letters in 1933.
Exhibited NAD 1917–23, 1925–42, 1944–47, 1949–
53, 1959–60.

CARL M. SCHULTHEISS (1885–1961)
(ANA 1944, NA 1946)
The Suckling Calf. Etching, 9/50. Signed, Carl M. Schultheiss.
National Academy of Design.

Schultheiss, born in Nürnberg, was educated and spent his early career in Germany. He came to the United States in the 1930s, and began by exhibiting his etchings at The Art Institute of Chicago in 1938. Schultheiss won the Talcott Prize, 1940, the John Taylor Arms Prize, 1943 and 1944, and awards from the Library of Congress, the Wichita Museum, the Laguna Beach Art Association, the National Academy, 1947, 1952, 1955, and the Society of American Graphic Artists, 1957, 1960. He received a grant from the National Institute of Arts and Letters and was given a one-man show by the Corcoran Gallery, Washington, D. C., 1946. He was Honorary President of the Society of American Graphic Artists.
Exhibited NAD 1941, 1944–56, 1958–62.

EVERETT SHINN (1876–1953)
(ANA 1935, NA 1943)
"I leaned over and plucked from her lips a kiss."
Illustration for *Frédérique* by Paul de Kock, Vol. I, Chap. 9. Charcoal on tan paper, 15¼ × 20⅛ inches. Signed, Everett Shinn/1906.
The Brooklyn Museum.

(For biography see p. 108.)

WALTER SHIRLAW (1838–1909)
(ANA 1887, NA 1888)
Seated Male Nude. Drawing, 24 × 20 inches.
Signed, W. Shirlaw, 1872.
National Academy of Design.

(For biography see p. 108.)

Everett Shinn, NA
"*I leaned over and plucked from her lips a kiss.*"
Illustration for *Fredérique* by Paul de Kock,
Vol. I, Chap. 9. Charcoal on tan paper
The Brooklyn Museum

JAMES D. SMILLIE (1833–1909)
(ANA 1865, NA 1876)
Old Houses near Boulogne. Etching and aquatint,
6½ × 4⅜ inches. Signed, James D. Smillie, 1890.
National Academy of Design.

Smillie was a native of New York, the son of a
jeweler and silversmith, and began etching before
the age of eight. At fourteen he did an ambitious
set of plates illustrating Milton's *Paradise Lost*. As
a young man Smillie was employed as a bank note
engraver. In 1862 he went to Europe to study for
two years and in 1864 abandoned engraving and
took up painting. He founded the American
Watercolor Society and served as president and
treasurer. He also helped organize the New York
Etching Club and was the United States repre-
sentative to supply examples of American etchers'
work to the Painter-Etchers Society of London.
Smillie etched most of Cole's "Voyage of Life".
Exhibited NAD 1853, 1864–81, 1883–87, 1889–92,
1896–98, 1901, 1904–05.

BENTON SPRUANCE (1904–1967)
(ANA 1948, NA 1959)
Anabasis I. Lithograph, 14¼ × 20¾, 4/40. Signed,
Spruance, 1951.
National Academy of Design.

Spruance was a native of Philadelphia and most
of his life centered around that city. He first studied art at the University of Pennsylvania School
of Fine Arts, 1924–25, and then at the Pennsylvania Academy, 1925–29. Spruance's training prepared him to be an expert technician in the medium of color lithography. He succeeded so well
that he won more than thirty first prizes in print
competitions plus other honors, including the
Beck, Pennell, and Eyre medals. For thirty-four
years he was chairman of the Fine Arts Department of Beaver College and later became director
of graphic arts at the Philadelphia College of Art.
Beaver College awarded him a Master of Arts
Degree in 1935 and the Philadelphia College of
Fine Arts an honorary Doctor of Fine Arts Degree in 1962. He received the Lindback Award for
distinguished teaching in 1962 and was an honorary member of the American Institute of Architects. Most major print collections contain examples of his work.
Exhibited NAD 1935–36, 1940–41, 1946, 1948–49,
1953–56, 1958–60, 1962–63.

J. Alden Weir, PNA
A Woman Sewing. Lithograph
Prints Division, The New York Public Library,
Astor, Lenox and Tilden Foundations

CADWALLADER WASHBURN (1866–1965)
(ANA 1940)
The Panama Hat (from Norlands series, 1907–10).
Drypoint 3/50, 7½ × 6⅛ inches. Signed,
Cadwallader Washburn.
Prints Division,
The New York Public Library, Astor, Lenox
and Tilden Foundations.

Washburn was born in Minneapolis and received
a Bachelor of Arts degree from Gallaudet College,
Washington, an institution for deaf mutes, Washburn having been so afflicted from the age of three.
He went on to the Massachusetts Institute of Technology to take a degree in architecture. Then he
came to New York to study art at the Art Students' League under Mowbray and Chase. He
also studied with Sorolla in Madrid and with
Besnard in Paris, exhibiting in the Salon from
1896 to 1904. An extensive traveler, he became a
war correspondent in Manchuria in 1904 to re-
port the Russo-Japanese War but returned to the
United States in 1906. In 1910–12 he reported the
early years of the Mexican Revolution. Washburn was a student of zoology and collected rare
birds' eggs. Among the museums which own his
work are the British Museum and Victoria and
Albert Museum, London, the Luxembourg and
Bibliothèque Nationale, Paris, the Rijksmuseum,
Amsterdam, the Metropolitan Museum, and the
Corcoran Gallery, Washington.
Exhibited NAD 1940–1, 1944–5, 1947, 1949, 1955.

J. ALDEN WEIR (1852–1919)
(ANA 1885, NA 1886, PNA 1915–17)
A Woman Sewing. Lithograph, 12¼ × 9 inches.
Signed, J A W on the stone.
Prints Division,
The New York Public Library, Astor, Lenox
and Tilden Foundations.

(For biography see p. 129.)

Watercolor

John James Audubon, HM(P)
American Black Rat. Watercolor
The American Museum of Natural History, New York

188

JOHN JAMES AUDUBON (1785–1851)
(HM(P) 1833)
American Black Rat. Watercolor,
21¾ × 27½ inches. Signed, J. J. A. Drawn from
Nature at "Minnie's Land," September 1, 1842.
The American Museum of Natural History,
New York.

(For biography see p. 26.)

GIFFORD BEAL (1879–1956)
(ANA 1908, NA 1914)
San Juan Road. Watercolor, 14 × 19 inches.
Signed, Gifford Beal, 1916.
Kraushaar Galleries, New York.

(For biography see p. 27.)

WALTER BIGGS (1886–1968)
(ANA 1944, NA 1947)
Yard at Home. Watercolor, 22 × 30 inches. Signed,
Walter Biggs, '45.
National Academy of Design.

Biggs was born in Elliston, Virginia, and first
studied at Virginia Polytechnic Institute before
going to New York City to enroll in the Chase
School and with Robert Henri, Kenneth Hayes
Miller, Edward Penfield and F. Luis Mora. A successful illustrator, he was part of the turmoil surrounding the Ashcan revolution in the early years
of this century and roomed with Bellows while
both were students of Henri. Biggs exhibited
widely and won prizes at the Salmagundi Club,
the Art Directors' Club and the National Academy. He taught at the Grand Central School of
Art and the Art Students' League. He was a member of the American Watercolor Society, the
Society of Illustrators and the Philadelphia Watercolor Club.
Exhibited NAD 1945–51, 1953, 1960–61, 1963,
1965.

CHARLES BURCHFIELD (1893–1967)
(ANA 1952, NA 1954)
Wet Snow and Ice. Watercolor, 38 × 30 inches.
Signed cb/1947–1955.
Kennedy Galleries, Inc., New York.

Burchfield was born in Ashtabula, Ohio, and
spent his youth in Salem, Ohio. He worked at a
metal fabricating plant during and after high
school until he had enough money to enroll at the
Cleveland School of Art, where he stayed for four
years. A scholarship at the National Academy
School lasted exactly one day. After six months of
service in the field artillery and camouflage units
of the AEF in 1918, he returned to Salem. During
this period of the late 'Teens he developed his first
characteristically evocative and fantastic nature
paintings. Later he became a designer of wallpaper
for M. H. Birge and Sons in Buffalo, and was
head of the design department. Burchfield read
Sherwood Anderson's *Winesburg, Ohio* about
1920, which changed his entire outlook on life and
art. Suddenly, early romanticism gave way to
paintings of the harsh realities of the man-made
world of houses, machinery, bridges, and the
Buffalo waterfront. This remained his chief interest until 1943, when he returned to his earlier
style, even reworking some of his nature paintings
of a quarter century before. In a letter to his
dealer, Frank Rehn in 1944 he referred to his city-
scapes as a "necessary diversion" in explaining his
return to romantic nature. Many honors and
prizes ($500 Award, Metropolitan Museum,
1952; Gold Medal, National Institute of Arts and
Letters, 1960) were bestowed on him.
Exhibited NAD 1927, 1948.

THOMAS EAKINS (1844–1916)
(ANA 1902, NA 1902)
The Zither Player. Watercolor,
11¾ × 9¹⁵⁄₁₆ inches. Signed, Eakins/76.
The Art Institute of Chicago.

(For biography see p. 56.)

Thomas Eakins, NA
The Zither Player. Watercolor
The Art Institute of Chicago

GEORGE GROSZ (1893–1959)(ANA 1950)
Couple (1934). Watercolor.
25¼ × 17¾ inches, 1934.
Whitney Museum of American Art, New York.

(For biography see p. 64.)

CHILDE HASSAM (1859–1935)
(ANA 1902, NA 1906)
Home of the Hummingbird. Watercolor,
14 × 10 inches. Signed, Childe Hassam 1893.
Arthur Altschul, New York.

(For biography see p. 69.)

WINSLOW HOMER (1836–1910)
(ANA 1864, NA 1865)
The Turtle Pound. Watercolor on paper,
14¹⁵⁄₁₆ × 21⅜ inches. Signed, Homer 1898.
The Brooklyn Museum.

(For biography see p. 76.)

Winslow Homer, NA
The Turtle Pound. Watercolor
The Brooklyn Museum

THEODORE KAUTZKY (1896–1953)
(ANA 1947, NA 1950)
March Snow, Vermont. Watercolor,
20½ × 28 inches. Signed, Ted Kautzky.
National Academy of Design.

Kautzky was born in Budapest, Hungary, and
received an architectural degree from the Royal
University of Hungary before emigrating to the
United States in 1923. He worked as an architect
for the New York City Parks Department and
taught at Pratt Institute, New York University,
the University of Pennsylvania, and the University of Toronto. Kautzky's watercolors became
widely known through several exhibitions in this
country and through his books on drawing and
watercolor painting. He won prizes at the Salmagundi Club, 1944, the Architectural League,
1938, American Watercolor Society, 1941, the
Baltimore Watercolor Club and the Obrig Prize,
1952. His work is owned by many public and
private collections.
Exhibited NAD 1948–54.

EMIL J. KOSA, JR. (1903–1968)
(ANA 1948, NA 1951)
Whistle Stop.
Watercolor, 21 × 29 inches.
National Academy of Design.
Acquired 1951 Diploma.

Kosa was born in Paris and studied at the Academy
of Fine Arts, Prague, with Thille and later at the
École des Beaux-Arts in Paris. He also studied
with Frank Kupka and J. P. Laurens and at the
California Art Institute after emigrating to the
United States as a young man. Kosa began winning awards at the age of twenty-five, and these
continued throughout his life, including four at
the National Academy, 1941, 1949, 1951, 1954.
Remaining on the West Coast most of his adult
life, his career was focused on that part of the
country. His work is owned by the California
State Library, Washington State College, Chaffey
Junior College, Santa Barbara Museum of Art,
the Los Angeles Museum of Art, and the Springfield (Massachusetts) Museum of Art. Kosa
painted a set of murals for the Lockheed Aircraft
Corporation.
Exhibited NAD 1938, 1940–42, 1944–45, 1947–56,
1958–60, 1962, 1969.

REGINALD MARSH (1898–1954)
(ANA 1937, NA 1943)
Locomotive, No. 2. Watercolor.
13½ × 19½ inches. Signed, Reginald Marsh 1929.
Whitney Museum of American Art, New York.

(For biography see p. 91.)

BARSE MILLER (1904–1973)
(ANA 1944, NA 1947)
Highway to Frisco.
Watercolor, 16½ × 20¾ inches. Signed.
National Academy of Design.
Acquired 1950 Diploma.

Miller was a native of New York City who studied at the Pennsylvania Academy and the National Academy. He also had private instruction under Henry Snell and Hugh Breckenridge. At eighteen he received and had renewed a Cresson Traveling Scholarship from the Pennsylvania Academy which enabled him to paint and study in Europe. His reputation is largely based on watercolors, but he also engaged in mural painting. During the Second World War Miller was officer in charge of the Combat Art Section of the Army Engineers in the Southwest Pacific theater of war and decorated with the Legion of Merit in 1945. He received medals for his watercolors from the California Art Club, the Los Angeles County Museum, the American Watercolor Society, the Santa Barbara Art Museum, and the National Academy. He was awarded a Guggenheim Fellowship in 1946. Miller taught at many art schools and colleges, including Queens College, New York. His work is widely distributed in museums and private collections.
Exhibited NAD 1945–47, 1949, 1951–55, 1958–62, 1964–69, 1971–73.

Thomas Moran, NA
Cliffs of the Rio Virgin. Watercolor
Cooper-Hewitt Museum of Design,
Smithsonian Institution, New York

THOMAS MORAN (1837–1926)
(ANA 1881, NA 1884)
Cliffs of the Rio Virgin (J. W. Powell Expedition,
1873). Watercolor. 8⅝ × 14 inches. Signed
with monogram, 1873.
Cooper-Hewitt Museum, New York.

Moran was the middle one of three painter broth-
ers, born to a weaver in Bolton, Lancashire, England. The family emigrated in 1844 and settled in
Maryland, where the father set up his loom.
Thomas Moran followed his brother, Edward, to
Philadelphia to be apprenticed as a wood engraver. After two years he began to paint in
watercolor. In 1862 he and Edward both went to
London where Moran spent most of his time
copying in the National Gallery, primarily
Turner, a major influence. Back in the United
States in 1871, he traveled with a geological expedition to the Yellowstone area and painted
"The Grand Canyon of the Yellowstone". A second trip two years later produced "Chasm of the
Colorado". These two canvases were purchased
by Congress for $10,000 each to hang in the Capi-
tol. Moran's frequent western jaunts provided
him with the rich lode of picturesque material for
his large colorful canvases. One practical purpose
they served was to awaken Eastern minds to possibilities and responsibilities in the West. Moran
settled in East Hampton, Long Island in 1884 and
summered there for many years. He continued to
travel, Mexico, Italy again, plus several trips to the
California Coast, spending his final decade in
Santa Barbara. In addition to his painting Moran
also became an expert etcher and lithographer.
Exhibited NAD 1866–68, 1872–73, 1875, 1877–85,
1887–1908, 1914, 1922, 1925.

ELIOT O'HARA (1890–1969)
(ANA 1944, NA 1948)
The Monkey-pod Tree—Hawaii. Watercolor,
25 × 19½ inches. Signed, Eliot O'Hara, 1939.
National Academy of Design.

O'Hara was a native of Waltham, Massachusetts,
whose early schooling and training were directed
towards the goal of joining his father's business,
the Waltham Dial Company, which he was man-
aging at the time of the elder O'Hara's death. He
had been interested in art from childhood, left the
business in 1927, and became one of the best
known American watercolor technicians and
teachers through his several schools and books on
watercolor instruction. O'Hara was a ceaseless
traveler, and he painted wherever he went, from
Russia to India to the Pacific Ocean plus most of
the Western hemisphere. His teaching methods
were so successful that the Encyclopedia Britan-
nica commissioned him to film twenty-four color
movies of watercolor instruction. His most famous school was at Goose Rocks Beach, Maine,
which burned down in 1947. His work is owned
by sixty-four museums in the United States and
Great Britain.
Exhibited NAD 1945–47, 1949–55, 1958, 1967–68.

EDWARD H. POTTHAST (1857–1927)
(ANA 1899, NA 1906)
Standing Room Only. Watercolor,
16 × 22¼ inches. Signed, E. Potthast.
Schweitzer Gallery, New York.

Potthast was born in Cincinnati, Ohio, and stud-
ied art first at the Cincinnati Academy. He then
went to Europe to work in Antwerp, Munich and
Paris. After his return to New York he won the
Clarke Prize at the National Academy, 1899, the
Evans Prize, American Watercolor Society, 1901,
the Silver Medal, St. Louis, 1904, and the Inness
Prize, Salmagundi Club, 1905. In November,
1910, he explored the Grand Canyon on a paint-
ing expedition with four other Academicians,
Thomas Moran, Elliott Daingerfield, Frederick B.
Williams and DeWitt Parshall. In the 1890's
Potthast illustrated articles for *Century* magazine.
He received the American Watercolor Society's
Hudnut Prize, 1914, and a silver medal at the
Panama-Pacific Exposition, San Francisco, 1915.
He was a member of the American Watercolor
Society, the New York Watercolor Club and the
Lotos Club. His work is owned by The Art Insti-
tute of Chicago, the Brooklyn Museum, the Cin-
cinnati Art Museum and other public and private
collections.
Exhibited NAD 1896–1927.

WILLIAM T. RICHARDS (1833–1905)
(HM(P) 1862, NA 1871)
Near Newport. Watercolor, 23 × 37 inches.
Signed, Wm. T. Richards, 1877.
National Academy of Design.

Richards, a native of Philadelphia, went to work
after high school as a designer of gas fixtures. He
studied wood engraving evenings and began to
paint independently. He exhibited his work at the
Philadelphia Art Union and received some instruction under Paul Weber. By 1853 he felt con-
fident enough in his possibilities as an artist that he
quit his $1500 job and took his savings to finance
a study trip in Europe. Richards worked with
teachers in Florence, Rome, and Paris, without
much commitment to any one. Back home in
1856 he settled in Germantown, Pa., did more
commercial designing, and found a patron in
George Whitney. Landscape and still life continued to be his subjects until, in 1867, he experi-
enced a storm at sea. The forms of the waves so
entranced him that they became his chief pre-
occupation. His detailed study and draughtsmanship, perhaps influenced by his early training in
precise design, became internationally recognized,
even claiming the admiration of John Ruskin
when one of his canvases was shown at the Royal
Academy. In his lifetime his work was acquired by
the Metropolitan Museum, the Corcoran Gallery,
and the Pennsylvania Academy. He spent his late
years at Newport, R. I., and painted much
abroad in the Orkney Islands, the Channel Islands,
and the west coast of Ireland.
Exhibited NAD 1858–63, 1867–79, 1881–82, 1884–
91, 1893–96, 1898–99, 1902–05.

John Singer Sargent, NA
In a Medici Villa. Watercolor
The Brooklyn Museum

JOHN SINGER SARGENT (1856–1925)
(ANA 1891, NA 1897)
In a Medici Villa. Watercolor, 21⅛ × 14⅝ inches.
The Brooklyn Museum.

(For biography see p. 105.)

WALTER SHIRLAW (1838–1909)
(ANA 1887, NA 1888)
Figures before a Spanish Building.
Watercolor, 9½ × 18¼ inches.
National Academy of Design. Gift from
K. P. Dreier Collection, 1953.

(For biography see p. 108.)

JOHN WHORF (1903–1959)
(ANA 1944, NA 1947)
Rainy Day, Park Street, Boston. Watercolor,
17 × 22 inches. Signed, John Whorf.
National Academy of Design. Exhibited 1946.

Whorf, a native of Boston, was a descendant of a
long line of Cape Cod ship captains. As a young
art student he went to Provincetown to study
painting with Charles Hawthorne, then one of
our most influential art teachers. Whorf initially
painted in oil and treated watercolor as a side issue.
His first one-man show of fifty-two paintings at
the age of twenty was completely sold out. In
spite of his success in oil he began to discover that
the quick brightness of watercolor was a more
congenial medium. It became his specialty, and he
painted wherever he traveled in the United States
and Europe. One of the most engaging aspects of
Whorf's art was his capacity to fasten his attention
upon absolutely any subject, from the most pro-
saic to the most romantic, from messy attics to
sinewy nudes, as suitable material. Most of the
leading museums own his work, and Harvard
University awarded him an honorary Master of
Arts Degree in 1938.
Exhibited NAD 1945–56, 1958–59.

Architecture

CHESTER H. ALDRICH (1871–1940)
(ANA 1928, NA 1939)
WILLIAM ADAMS DELANO (1874–1960)
(ANA 1934, NA 1937)
Knickerbocker Club, New York (1914–15).

Aldrich was born and educated in Providence, Rhode Island, and at the Massachusetts Institute of Technology. After graduation he went to Paris to study at the École des Beaux-Arts, from which he received a diploma in 1900. In 1903 he entered into partnership with William A. Delano. The following year their design for the Walters Art Gallery, Baltimore, started them on a highly successful career. The Union, Colony and Knickerbocker Clubs were their principal New York commissions. In addition they designed the Japanese Embassy, Washington, D. C., the new United States Embassy, Paris, and several academic buildings for Smith College, the Hotchkiss School, Yale University, and Cornell University. Their other outstanding public commission was the new Post Office Building, Washington, D. C., 1933. Their residential commissions included the estates of John D. Rockefeller, Pocantico Hills, N. Y., Otto Kahn, Cold Spring Harbor, N. Y., Vincent Astor, Port Washington, N. Y., and Mrs. Dwight Morrow, Englewood, N. J. Aldrich ended his career by retiring from practice and taking on the post of Director of the American Academy in Rome in 1935—where he died 1940. He was a Fellow of the American Institute of Architects, and a member of the National Institute of Arts and Letters.

Delano received a BA degree from Yale University in 1895 and then went to Paris to study at the École des Beaux-Arts, from which he received a diploma in 1903. After returning to New York, he taught design at Columbia University while studying for a BFA degree at Yale University, which he received in 1908. In 1903 he had formed with Charles H. Aldrich a practicing partnership which produced a number of architectural landmarks. Delano was a member of the National Park and Planning Commission, the National Commission of Fine Arts, the Art Commission of the City of New York, and the American Academy of Arts and Letters. He was an officer of the French Legion of Honor and a Fellow of the American Institute of Architects.

HENRY BACON (1866–1924)
(ANA 1913, NA 1917)
JAMES L. GREENLEAF (1857–1933) (ANA 1924)
Lincoln Memorial, Washington, D. C. (1923).

Bacon was born at Watseka, Illinois, and went to Boston to study at Chauncey Hall School at the age of fifteen. After a year at the University of Illinois he quit to go to work in 1885 as a draughtsman for Chamberlin and Whidden, Boston. Later he joined McKim, Mead and White in New York and while there won the Rotch Traveling Scholarship, a two year sojourn in Europe. Following six more years with McKim, Mead and White he formed a partnership with James Brite which lasted until 1902. Brite and Bacon designed the Public Library, Jersey City, New Jersey, following a competition. Bacon designed many public and commercial buildings, churches, hospitals, etc., independently, but his fame survives mainly as a designer of monuments in collaboration with sculptors Augustus Saint-Gaudens and Daniel Chester French. With the latter he was associated on more than fifty monuments around the country, such as the General Hooker monument in front of the State House, Boston, the Alice Freeman Palmer Memorial at Wellesley College, and the statue of Lincoln on the grounds of the state capitol, Lincoln, Nebraska. His last and greatest achievement was the design for the Lincoln Memorial in Potomac Park, Washington, D. C., also a French collaboration. For this Bacon received the gold medal of the American Institute of Architects. He was also a member of the National Institute of Arts and Letters.

Greenleaf was born in Kortright, Delaware County, New York, and graduated from Columbia University's School of Mines in 1880. As a special agent for the tenth United States census Greenleaf made a survey during 1880–82 of water power in the Northwest. He then taught engineering at Columbia until 1894. In the late 'Nineties he turned to landscape architecture and designed many of the large estates of suburban New York City. In 1918 President Wilson appointed him to the National Commission of Fine Arts, and in this capacity Greenleaf advised on matters concerning both National Parks and American cemeteries in France. He was a Fellow of the American Society of Landscape Architects.

Henry Bacon, NA (Architect)
James L. Greenleaf, ANA (Landscape Architect)
Lincoln Memorial, Washington, D.C.

ARTHUR BROWN, JR. (1874–1957)
(ANA 1943, NA 1953)
Opera House, San Francisco (1932)

Brown was a San Francisco architect fortunate enough to have lived and worked in the Bay City at a time when the community was rebuilding itself after the 1906 earthquake. He was a lecturer and teacher, a consultant for two world's fairs and also for the construction of the Bay Bridge, for the Treasury Department, and for the University of California. Brown designed, partially or completely, the City Hall, the War Memorial Opera House, the Veterans' Auditorium, the Federal Office Building, Temple Emanu-el, and the Coit tower on Telegraph Hill. He was given an honorary doctorate of Laws by the University of California and was a Fellow of the American Institute of Architects, a member of the American Academy of Arts and Letters, and an officer of the French Legion of Honor.

CHARLES BULFINCH (1763–1844) (HM(P) 1827)
Massachusetts State House, Boston (1795)

Bulfinch, the son of socially prominent parents in Boston, received the approved academic education at Harvard College, 1778–81. A leisurely tour of England and the continent, 1785–86, convinced him to study architecture. Jefferson, then in Paris, took an interest in him and made recommendations for study. As a result of his travels he settled in Boston in 1787 and, between 1790 and 1825, practically rebuilt the city as chief alderman (Mayor) of Boston. He developed what has come to be known as the "Federal Style" by incorporating the then popular neo-classical forms with local needs and symbols. More to the point he is credited with having invented the profession of architecture in the United States. Bulfinch's early public work is considered to be his best, for example the old Hollis Street Church, 1788, the Connecticut State House, Hartford, 1792, the Massachusetts State House, Boston, 1795 and the State Capitol, Augusta, Maine. In addition to many other churches and public buildings, the Bulfinch influence on domestic architecture can be seen on Beacon Hill, Boston, a unique part of the city. In 1817 President Monroe appointed him Supervising Architect of work at the national capitol where his chief project was to restore the two wings of the capitol burned by the British in 1814.

JOHN M. CARRÈRE (1858–1911)
(ANA 1908, NA 1910)
THOMAS HASTINGS (1860–1929)
(ANA 1906, NA 1909)
New York Public Library (1911)

Carrère was born in Rio De Janeiro, the son of a coffee merchant from Baltimore. Educated in Europe, he early demonstrated skill at drawing houses. He entered the École des Beaux-Arts at the age of twenty and was awarded a diploma in 1882. The following year he was working for McKim, Mead and White. There he discovered a former Beaux-Arts colleague, Thomas Hastings, also working as a draughtsman. Within a few months the two young men decided to form their own architectural partnership. They started out as part of the first land development enthusiasm in Florida. For twenty-five years they contributed lasting architectural features to New York, Washington, Saint Louis, Palm Beach, Newport, and Toronto. In addition to New York's Public Library and Frick Collection (formerly residence), they designed the Richmond Borough Hall, N. Y., 1903–07, St. George's Terminal Ferry, Staten Island, 1904, Traders Bank, Toronto, 1905, and the House and Senate Office Buildings, Washington, 1905–06. Private residences included those for Elihu Root, Murray Guggenheim, Mrs. Richard Gambrill, and William K. Vanderbilt. Carrère was a Fellow of the American Institute of Architects and served on its board of directors, a member of the Architectural League, and also of the American Academy of Arts and Letters.

Hastings was born in New York City and educated in private schools, two years of architectural study at Columbia University, and further study at the École des Beaux-Arts, Paris. On his return in 1883 he joined the office of McKim, Mead and White and left after a year to set up a successful partnership with John M. Carrère. The firm received its first important commission from Henry Flagler in St. Augustine, Florida. They opened offices in New York and began to alter the face of the city. The Richmond Borough Hall, the First Church of Christ, Scientist, the Manhattan Bridge arch and approaches, the Century Theater, the Staten Island Terminal Building, and the New York Public Library commission (won in an open competition) are among their better known works. The partners also designed the House and Senate office buildings, Washington, the Traders Bank, Toronto, the Royal Bank of Canada, Montreal, and the Woolsey and Memorial Halls, Yale University. He was a member and director of the American Institute of Architects, and one of the founders of the Architectural League, New York.

Paul P. Cret, NA
Pan-American Union, Washington, D.C.

PAUL P. CRET (1876–1945)
(ANA 1935, NA 1938)
Pan-American Union Building, Washington, D. C.
(1907–10)

Cret was born and educated in Lyons, France. He studied architecture at both the Lyons and Paris École des Beaux-Arts and came to this country to teach at the University of Pennsylvania. In 1907 he resigned from the University to initiate his own career in architecture. However he continued to teach all his life. An early project was a collaboration with Albert Kelsey in the design of the Pan-American Union Building, Washington, D. C., 1907–1910. Later he worked with Zanziger, Borie and Medary on the Indianapolis Central Public Library, 1913–1916, the Detroit Institute of Arts, 1921, and the Valley Forge Memorial Arch, Philadelphia, 1910. Independently he designed the Integrity Trust Building, 1929, the Rodin Museum, 1932, and the Federal Reserve Bank, all in Philadelphia. In Washington he designed the Federal Reserve Bank, 1935–37, and the Folger Shakespeare Memorial Library, 1932. He was a member of the board of architects for Chicago's Century of Progress, 1933, and was appointed to the Federal Fine Arts Commission, 1940. Cret also designed a number of war memorials following the First War, notably a monument to Quentin Roosevelt, 1921, at Chambery, France.

CASS GILBERT (1859–1934)
(ANA 1906, NA 1908, PNA 1926–33)
Woolworth Building, New York (1911–13)

Gilbert was a native of Zanesville, Ohio, whose family moved to St. Paul, Minnesota, when he was a child. Educated in St. Paul, he completed special architectural training at the Massachusetts Institute of Technology. In 1880 he traveled for several months through France, Italy and England. In September of that year he was employed by McKim, Mead and White, where he later served as personal assistant to Stanford White. Two years following he formed a partnership with James K. Taylor in St. Paul. After the dissolution of the partnership Gilbert worked independently in St. Paul and won a competition for the Minnesota State Capitol in 1896. This started a rush of commissions for large public buildings —Essex County Court House, Newark, New Jersey, Custom House, Festival Hall and Art Museum, St. Louis, Central Public Library, St. Louis, U. S. Treasury Annex, Washington, D. C., U. S. Chamber of Commerce, Washington, U. S. Legation Building, Toronto, West Virginia State Capitol, Supreme Court Building, Washington, 1933, and the Federal Court House, New York. Gilbert also worked for many insurance companies, but his most familiar landmark was the neo-Gothic design for the then tallest building in the world, the Woolworth Building. His professional associations were the American Institute of Architects and the Architectural League.

209

ALFRED GEIFFERT, JR. (1890–1957) (ANA 1951)
JOHN RUSSELL POPE (1874–1937)
(ANA 1919, NA 1924)
National Gallery of Art, Washington, D. C. (1941)

Geiffert was born in Cincinnati, Ohio, and moved with his family to Jersey City, New Jersey, where he went through public school. He entered the office of Ferruccio Vitale at the age of eighteen— "as office boy," he said—and discovered the pleasures of landscape design. Geiffert continued his education with extension courses at Columbia University, but never earned a degree. In a few years he became a partner in the firm and stayed until Vitale's death in 1933. In the same offices on Park Avenue, New York City, Geiffert continued his landscape design for his remaining twenty-four years. He was a member and medalist of the Architectural League of New York and the National Sculpture Society. He was a Fellow of the American Society of Landscape Architects and served as president from 1928 to 1932.

Pope was born in New York, attended City College, and studied architecture at Columbia University's School of Mines under William R. Ware. He won the McKim Roman Scholarship in 1895 and the Schermerhorn Scholarship the following year which enabled him to study at the American Academy in Rome for two years. Then there followed two years at the École des Beaux-Arts with a diploma in 1900. Returning to New York, Pope worked for Bruce Price, finally met McKim, and began to execute commissions greatly influenced by the latter's neo-classicism. During the succeeding thirty-five years he established a reputation as an architect of a cool traditionalism exactly suited for such works as the National Gallery of Art, Constitution Hall, and the Jefferson Memorial of Washington, D. C., as well as additions to the Metropolitan and Frick Museums of New York. In London Pope designed the Duveen Wing of the British Museum, the Sculpture Hall of the Tate Gallery, and the United States Government Building. Many honors, domestic and European, were bestowed on him: a Fellow of the American Institute of Architects, the Medal of Honor of the Architectural League, a Chevalier of the French Legion of Honor, a member of the National Institute of Arts and Letters and President of the American Academy in Rome.

John Russell Pope, NA
National Gallery of Art, Washington, D.C.

BERTRAM G. GOODHUE (1869–1924)
(ANA 1917, NA 1923)
St. Thomas Episcopal Church, New York (1921)

Goodhue was born in Pomfret, Connecticut, and received basic education in New Haven. At the age of fifteen he started a six year period of working for ecclesiastical architect James Renwick of New York. Here he developed his highly regarded skills in draughtsmanship and decorative design. In 1891 Goodhue began a twenty-three year period of association with Ralph Adams Cram, first in the Boston office of Cram and Wentworth, then as a partner in Cram, Goodhue and Ferguson. His Gothic revival designs were characteristic of these years, most notably St. Thomas Church, New York, 1906. His churches dot the northeast, in Massachusetts, Rhode Island, Connecticut, New York, New Jersey, and Washington, D. C. In 1914 Goodhue opened his own office in New York and continued his ecclesiastical designs, increasingly, though, including secular structures among commissions. The Physics Building at the California Institute of Technology, Pasadena, the Central Public Library, Los Angeles, the Marine Air Corps Base and Naval Air Station, San Diego, and the Fine Arts Building at the Panama-Pacific Exposition, 1915, were his designs. His most notable achievement was his revolutionary design for the Nebraska State Capitol, completed after his death.

WALTER GROPIUS (1883–1969)
(ANA 1967, NA 1968)
Graduate Center, Harvard (1949)

Gropius was born in Berlin, Germany, into a family of architects and builders. He studied architecture at the Universities of Charlottenburg-Berlin and Munich from 1903 to 1907 and then traveled in Europe. He worked for a time in a pottery in Spain. His first architectural job was in the office of Peter Behrens. His designs for the Fagus building, Algeld-am-der Leine, and the Hall of Machinery, Werkbund Exposition, brought him his first public attention. Gropius served in the German army in the First War and earned the Iron Cross. After the war he organized the Bauhaus School of Design out of what had been the Grand Ducal Art School in Weimar. This institution is the one which established Gropius as the philosopher-saint of modern art in Germany. The Bauhaus was a neo-medieval gathering together of many kinds of artists and artisans under a single banner to work cooperatively on art and design ideas for modern life. He retired from the school in 1928, and the Nazis closed it in 1933 after it had moved to Dessau. He came to the United States in 1937 to head Harvard University's Graduate School of Design, from which he retired in 1952. Gropius then formed the Architects' Collaborative and continued as designer and mentor for that group until his death.

HENRY J. HARDENBERGH (1847–1918)
(ANA 1910)
Plaza Hotel, New York (1906)

Hardenbergh was born in New Brunswick, New Jersey, received schooling locally, and at the age of eighteen entered the office of D. Lienau as a student draughtsman. In 1870 he opened his own New York office. After smaller work in New Jersey and New York, Hardenbergh made his first real success with a design for the Dakota Apartment House, Central Park West, New York, 1884. This set off a chain reaction of apartment house and hotel commissions which culminated in his design for the Plaza Hotel, 1906, and the Copley Plaza Hotel, Boston, 1912. Hardenbergh was a Fellow of the American Institute of Architects, member and president of the Architectural League of New York, and one of the founders of the Municipal Art Society, New York.

JOHN HAVILAND (1792–1852) (HM(P) 1827)
Pennsylvania Institute for the Deaf and Dumb
(now the Museum School of Art), Philadelphia
(1829–33)

Haviland was a native of England who received his architectural training in the office of James Elmes. In 1816 he emigrated to this country, settled in Philadelphia, and opened his own architectural office. For the next twenty years he developed a reputation as a specialist in penitentiary design. In addition he simultaneously designed several Philadelphia churches, the Franklin Institute, and the Philadelphia Arcade. In 1824 he designed the Asylum for the Deaf and Dumb which now houses the Philadelphia Museum School of Art. Haviland's designs for prisons continued in Missouri, Rhode Island, and New York, but he also added other churches, theaters, and private residences to his oeuvre.

George Howe, ANA
Philadelphia Savings Fund Society Building

GEORGE HOWE (1886–1955) (ANA 1951)
Philadelphia Savings Fund Society Building (1932)

Howe, a native of Worcester, Massachusetts, graduated from Harvard University, 1908, and led an architectural life largely in partnership with several of the country's leading designers, notably William Lescaze, Norman Bel Geddes, and Louis Kahn. With Lescaze he designed his most influential work, the steel and glass building for the Philadelphia Savings Fund Society, 1932. It was the only International Style skyscraper to be built until Mies van der Rohe's work after the Second War. In addition Howe designed the Oakland School, Croton, New York, 1929 (a pioneer International Style structure), Carver Court Housing Project, Coatesville, Pennsylvania 1943, and residences in Chestnut Hill and other Philadelphia suburbs. One of his most imaginative houses is "Fortune Rock", the Thomas house on Soames Sound, Maine. This was built entirely of local materials by local craftsmen and is distinguished by sensitive siting and a dramatically cantilevered living room projecting forty feet over water. The firm of Mellor, Meigs and Howe received the annual medal of the Architectural League, 1925. In the 1940's Howe was Supervising Architect for the Public Buildings Administration and Chairman of the Yale University Department of Architecture, 1950–54. He was resident architect of the American Academy in Rome.

BURNHAM HOYT (1887–1960) (ANA 1953)
Red Rocks Amphitheater, Denver, Colorado (1941)

Hoyt was a native of Denver, Colorado, and a professor of design at New York University from 1929 to 1933. He worked for three New York architectural firms: George Post, Goodhue and Pelton, and Allen and Collens. In association with the latter two firms he was responsible for the interior design of the Riverside Church, New York City.

LOUIS I. KAHN (1902–1974) (ANA 1965)
Salk Institute, La Jolla, California (1959)

Kahn was born on the island of Osel, Estonia, and came to the United States as a boy. He received a traditional Beaux-Arts-style architectural education at the University of Pennsylvania, graduating in 1924. After traveling in Europe, he went to work for Paul Cret during the 'Thirties and executed a project for the Philadelphia Planning Commission. In 1941 he briefly worked in partnership with pioneer modern architect George Howe and helped with the Carver Court Housing Project, Coatesville, Pennsylvania, 1943. He began to design independently in 1947. In 1950–51 he was resident architect of the American Academy in Rome, and, later, design critic at Yale University. In 1955 he became professor of architecture at the University of Pennsylvania. Kahn's principal works are the Yale Art Gallery, 1954, the Trenton Bath Houses, 1956, the Richards Medical Research Building, University of Pennsylvania, 1960, the Salk Institute, La Jolla, California, 1959, and the Olivetti-Underwood Corp. factory building, Harrisburg, Pennsylvania, 1969.

WILLIAM M. KENDALL (1856–1941)
(ANA 1930, NA 1935)
Columbia University (1893–97)

Kendall was born in Jamaica Plain, Massachusetts, graduated from Harvard College in 1876, and took two years of architectural study at the Massachusetts Institute of Technology. Work in architectural offices in Boston and New York, plus a European year of travel and study, prepared him for membership in the firm of McKim, Mead and White in 1882. He was successively promoted in the organization until, in 1906, on the death of Stanford White, he was made a partner. Kendall worked on many of the firm's important projects: old Madison Square Garden, New York, the Morgan Library, New York, the Washington Memorial Arch, New York, the Butler Art Institute, Youngstown, Ohio, City Hall, Burlington, Vermont, the American Academy in Rome, the main United States Post Office, New York, Municipal Building, New York, the Savoy Plaza Hotel, Low Library, Columbia University, the Harvard School of Business, and the Plymouth Rock Memorial, Plymouth, Massachusetts. Later he designed several war memorials in Italy and France. He was a member of many professional societies and a Fellow of the American Institute of Architects.

CHARLES Z. KLAUDER (1872–1938) (ANA 1938)
Dormitory Group, Princeton (1933–34)

Klauder was born in Philadelphia of German immigrant parents. He studied briefly at the School of Industrial Art of the Pennsylvania Museum and then entered the office of architect T. P. Chandler in 1887. He stayed there until 1893, and from then until 1900 was associated with three other firms. At the turn of the century he began a long association with Day and Brother. Eleven years later he became a partner in the firm named Day and Klauder. Finally in 1927, after F. M. Day died, the firm was inherited by Klauder. He was executive architect for Holder Hall and other buildings on the Princeton University campus, the Cathedral of Learning and other structures for the University of Pittsburgh, plus buildings for many other American academic institutions. He received many awards and was a Fellow of the American Institute of Architects and the Architectural League of New York.

C. GRANT LAFARGE (1862–1938) (ANA 1910)
Chancel, Cathedral of St. John the Divine, New York (1892–1907)

LaFarge, the son of painter John LaFarge was born in Newport, Rhode Island. After two years of study at the Massachusetts Institute of Technology and a period of working for Henry H. Richardson in Brookline, Mass., he opened his own office in New York in 1884. Shortly afterwards he formed a partnership with George L. Heins. The firm of Heins and LaFarge won the competition for the design of the Cathedral of St. John the Divine, New York, 1892; but when Heins died fifteen years later, after the completion of the choir, the Board of Trustees transferred the design supervision to Ralph Adams Cram. In spite of this professional rebuff, LaFarge continued to work, finally incorporating his son into the firm as LaFarge and Son. He designed many churches from Rhode Island to Washington, D. C., plus a number of secular buildings. Among the latter are the United States Naval Hospital, Brooklyn, the New York subway stations built for the Rapid Transit Commission, all buildings of the New York Zoological Park, the Packard Memorial Library, Salt Lake City, and the New York Genealogical Society Building. LaFarge was a member of the Architectural League and a Fellow of the American Institute of Architects.

Charles F. McKim, NA
William R. Mead, NA
Morgan Library, New York

CHARLES F. MCKIM (1847–1909)
(ANA 1905, NA 1907)
WILLIAM R. MEAD (1846–1928)
(ANA 1908, NA 1910)
Morgan Library, New York (1906)

McKim was a native of Isabella Furnace, Pennsylvania. He received his public schooling in Philadelphia and dropped out of Harvard to become an architectural apprentice in the office of Russell Sturgis. Later he went to Paris to study at the École des Beaux-Arts. At the same time he traveled in England, Germany, Austria, and northern Italy. In 1870 McKim returned to the United States and went to work in the office of Gambrill and Richardson. Simultaneously he began independent designing and in 1872 invited William Mead to join him in certain projects. In 1879 Stanford White was added to the firm and the fuse lit for one of the most remarkable architectural explosions in this country's history. The next quarter century saw the construction by the firm of McKim, Mead and White of some of the finest buildings on this continent: the Boston Public Library, the Rhode Island State Capitol, the Washington Memorial Arch, New York, the Newport Casino, the New York University Library and Hall of Fame, the University, Century, Knickerbocker and Lambs' Clubs, the Low Library of Columbia University, the Pennsylvania Railroad Terminal, New York, the Army War College, Washington, D. C., Madison Square Garden, New York, 1891, and the influential New York State building at the World's Columbian Exposition, Chicago, 1893. One of his greatest efforts, as a member of the McMillan Commission, was the restoration of L'Enfant's plan of Washington. He completely renovated the White House. The 1906 murder of Stanford White affected McKim so deeply that he retired and spent his final months in seclusion at his home in St. James, Long Island. McKim was a Fellow of the American Institute of Architects. He founded and personally supported the American Academy in Rome.

Mead was born in Brattleboro, Vermont, and received his early schooling there. He graduated from Amherst College and acquired his architectural training in the office of Russell Sturgis, New York. In 1871 he went to Europe for an eighteen-month study tour. On his return he formed a partnership with fellow-Sturgis-draughtsman Charles F. McKim. Mead's particular assignment in the firm was the management of the office. Mead continued as active head of the firm after the deaths of his two partners in 1906 and 1909 until his retirement in 1920. He succeeded McKim as President of the American Academy in Rome for eighteen years. He was a Fellow of the American Institute of Architects, and a member of the American Academy of Arts and Letters.

WILLIAM F. LAMB (1883–1952)
(ANA 1942, NA 1950)
Empire State Building, New York (1931)

Lamb was a partner in the architectural firm of Shreve, Lamb and Harmon, designers of the Empire State, Bankers Trust, General Motors, Best and Company, and many New York City buildings. In addition the firm designed buildings for Cornell University, the Kent School, and other academic institutions. Lamb was a Fellow of the American Institute of Architects, a member of the Federal Commission of Fine Arts and of the Municipal Art Commission of New York City.

LUDWIG MIES VAN DER ROHE (1886–1969)
(ANA 1963, NA 1964)
Seagram Building, New York (1958)

Mies was born in Aachen, Germany, and his introduction to the arts of building was received from his father, a master mason and stone cutter. He first learned to draw for stucco decoration. In 1905 he went to Berlin and worked for an architect of wood structures. This led to a two-year apprenticeship to furniture designer Bruno Paul. After a one-year stint as an independent architect, Mies began to work in 1908 for Peter Behrens, then Germany's most forward looking architect. From 1919 on he forged his own alloy of classicism, cubism, De Stijl, and modern engineering techniques which ultimately won him a place as one of the four great seminal architects of the twentieth century. Among his European designs were the memorial to Karl Liebknecht and Rosa Luxemburg, Berlin, 1926, the Lange House, Krefeld, 1928, the German Pavilion at the Barcelona Fair, 1929, and the Tugendhat house, Brno, 1930. For the last three years of the Bauhaus's existence Mies was its director until the Nazis closed it in 1933. He emigrated to the United States in 1937 and in 1944 became a citizen. His designs for the campus of the Illinois Institute of Technology, Chicago (where he was invited to teach), 1952–56, the Lake Shore Apartments, Chicago, 1957, and the Seagram Building, 1958, set a standard for modern architectural design.

CHARLES ADAMS PLATT (1861–1933)
(ANA 1897, NA 1911)
Freer Gallery, Washington, D. C.(1923)

Platt was born in New York, studied art at the National Academy of Design and then, beginning in 1882, spent five years in Europe studying and painting. On his return to this country he joined the workshop of Augustus Saint-Gaudens in Cornish, New Hampshire. In 1892 he went to Europe again, where his landscape paintings and etchings won him prizes and recognition. He visited Italy to study Renaissance gardens and published a book on that subject. He finally drifted into the architectural profession in 1916 through the patronage of William Astor, for whom he designed several buildings. Later he built the Freer Gallery, Washington, D. C., the Connecticut College for Women, the Lyman Allyn Museum, New London, and a general plan for the campus of the University of Illinois which included the erection of nine buildings between 1922 and 1930. Platt also served as consulting architect for Dartmouth College, Johns Hopkins University, the University of Rochester, and, most extensively, of Phillips Academy, Andover, Massachusetts. He retired to Cornish, New Hampshire, full of honors. He succeeded William R. Mead as President of the American Academy in Rome from 1928 until his death. Platt was a Fellow of the American Institute of Architects.

EERO SAARINEN (1910–1961)
(ANA 1952, NA 1958)
Dulles International Airport, Washington, D. C.
(1958–62)

Saarinen was born in Kirkkonummi, Finland, and came to this country in 1923 with his architect father. He received a degree from Yale University in 1934, traveled in Europe the following two years, and entered into partnership with his father in Birmingham, Michigan. Saarinen's influence on his father's work can be detected from the late 1930's on, but it was his winning of the Jefferson Memorial Competition, St. Louis, 1949, which established him as an independent designer. His first major industrial work was the General Motors Technical Center, Warren, Michigan, 1955, a centralized "campus plan". From that he went on to design for the Massachusetts Institute of Technology (Kresge Auditorium and Chapel), the Yale University Hockey Rink, the TWA Terminal, Kennedy Airport, New York, Dulles Airport, Washington, D. C., and United States Embassies in London and Oslo.

Eero Saarinen, NA
Dulles International Airport, Washington, D.C.

ELIEL SAARINEN (1873–1950)
(ANA 1940, NA 1946)
Kleinhans Music Hall, Buffalo (1938)

Saarinen was born in Rantasalmi, Finland, studied painting at the University and architecture at the Polyteknisk Institut, Helsinki, from which he graduated in 1897. His partnership with Gesellius and Lindgren received international recognition for their Finnish Pavilion at the Paris Exposition, 1899. Their designs for a residence and studio, Hvitträsk, and for the Helsinki Railway Station, 1904, further enhanced Saarinen's standing. He was involved in a city planning scheme for Canberra, Australia, but finally made a name for himself in the United States as the runner-up in the competition for the design for the Chicago Tribune Tower. He moved to the United States in 1923 and began to work on the Cranbrook Academy Schools, Michigan. In 1937 he formed a partnership with his son, Eero, and subsequently produced work only within the context of that firm. His own design was influenced by his son in such structures as the Kleinhans Music Hall, Buffalo, the Christ Lutheran Church, Minneapolis, and the General Motors Technical Center, Warren, Michigan.

HENRY R. SHEPLEY (1887–1962)
(ANA 1939, NA 1943)
New York Hospital (1932)

Shepley was born in Brookline, Massachusetts, and graduated from Harvard College, 1910. He went to Paris to study at the École des Beaux-Arts, from which he received a diploma in 1914. As a partner in the firm of Coolidge, Shepley, Bulfinch and Abbott he designed New York Hospital-Cornell Medical Center, New York City, Hartford Hospital, the Warren Building for Massachusetts General Hospital, Boston, several buildings for Harvard University, and the United States cemetery and memorial chapel, Margraten, Holland. Shepley was honored with a doctorate in arts, Harvard University, a gold medal from the American Academy of Arts and Letters, a special award from the Netherlands government, the degree of Chevalier of the French Legion of Honor, and a gold medal from the New York Architectural League. He was a member of the National Commission of Fine Arts, a member of the commission for Lincoln Square development, and was appointed to a commission of three to advise on all phases of extensions to the United States Capitol.

William Strickland, HM(P)
Second Bank of the United States, Philadelphia, Pa.

WILLIAM STRICKLAND (1787–1854) (HM(P) 1827)
Second Bank of the United States, Philadelphia
(1819–24)

Strickland was born in Philadelphia, the son of a carpenter who worked for Benjamin Latrobe. This circumstance led to his being tutored by Latrobe in the mysteries of architecture. By 1807 he was sufficiently schooled that he could go with his father to New York and assist him in the remodeling of the old Park Theater. Strickland also became interested in theatrical scene painting and other art forms at this time. Back in Philadelphia he opened an architectural office of his own at the age of twenty-two. He designed the old Masonic Hall, St. Stephen's Church, the United States Naval Asylum, the United States Mint, and the Merchants' Exchange (called the "pride of Philadelphia" at the time of its construction in 1836). He also planned the restoration of Independence Hall. Strickland's last and most important building was the Tennessee State House in Nashville, literally his own monument because he is buried in a crypt beneath it. He was a founding member of the National Society of Architects, the predecessor of the American Institute of Architects.

MARTIN E. THOMPSON (1786–1877)
(Founder NA 1926)
Naval Hospital Building, New York Naval Shipyard, Brooklyn, N. Y. (1830–38)

Thompson, a native of New York City, got his start as a carpenter. His architectural training was the result of on-the-job experience working for Thomas R. Brady on the Merchants' Exchange Building. Thompson's first building under his own name was the Second Bank of the United States, 1824. The façade of this structure has been preserved in the south front of the American wing of the Metropolitan Museum. In 1827 Thompson entered into partnership with Ithiel Town, and with him was responsible for the Phoenix Bank in Hartford, the Church of the Ascension, Canal Street, New York, and the steeple of St. Mark's in the Bowery. Independently he later designed the Columbia Grammar School, Sailors' Snug Harbor, Staten Island, the State Arsenal Building, Central Park (now the Parks Department office), and several plans for the enlargement of City Hall.

Martin E. Thompson, NA
Old Naval Hospital Building, New York Naval Shipyard, Brooklyn, N.Y.

Ithiel Town, NA
Sub-Treasury Building, New York

ITHIEL TOWN (1784–1844) (Founder NA 1826)
Sub-Treasury Building (Federal Hall National Memorial, New York) (1834–42)

Town was a native of Thompson, Connecticut, the son of a farmer, and began working as a carpenter in his 'teens. He studied architecture in Boston with Benjamin Asher and went to work in the office of architect and engineer Captain Isaac Damon in Northampton, Massachusetts, in 1814. Town assisted Damon in the construction of the Center Meeting House, New Haven, 1817. In 1827 he moved to New York and formed a partnership with Martin L. Thompson. They established their office in the Merchants' Exchange Building where they displayed drawings, engravings, etc., and Town installed his architectural library, ultimately to become the most complete in the country at that time. Two years later Town's partner became Alexander Davis, a draughtsman in the firm. Town and Davis designed the New York Customs House, Yale College Library, New Haven, the Wadsworth Athenaeum, Hartford, and the state capitols of North Carolina, Indiana, and Illinois. In spite of his fame as an architect, Town's principal income derived from his work as an engineer. He was the best known bridge builder of his time.

FRANK LLOYD WRIGHT (1867–1959) (ANA 1952)
Johnson Wax Company Administration Building, Racine, Wisconsin (1936–39)

Wright was born in Richland Center, Wisconsin. He was educated in the Froebel kindergarten system, public schools with the aid of readings in Ruskin and Viollet-le-Duc, and two years of engineering at the University of Wisconsin. By then he had had enough of formal education, and dropped out in 1888 to work in Chicago for the creative architectural firm, Adler and Sullivan. He quickly was put in charge of domestic commissions, notably the Charnley house, Chicago, 1892. Setting out on his own in 1893, he built a number of private projects in Wisconsin and Chicago until 1900, when the first evidences of his "prairie style" houses emerged. During the next decade, climaxed by the Robie house in 1909, Wright designed a series of low lying, deeply eaved houses in Chicago's suburbs which revolutionized architecture internationally. Simultaneously he produced the reinforced concrete structures of the Larkin Office Building, Buffalo, 1904, the Unity Church, Oak Park, Ill., 1906, and a small hotel in Mason City, Iowa, 1909. Other landmark structures by Wright are the Imperial Hotel, Tokyo, 1922 (which withstood the earthquake of 1923) the Kaufmann house, "Falling Water", Bear Run, Pennsylvania, 1936, the campus of Florida Southern College, Lakeland, Florida, 1938, the Price Tower, Bartlesville, Oklahoma, 1955, and the Guggenheim Museum, New York, 1959.

Frank Lloyd Wright, ANA
Johnson Wax Co. Administration Building, Racine, Wisc.

The New York Scene of 1825

To commemorate the 150th Anniversary of the founding of the National Academy of Design, the Museum of the City of New York has organized an exhibition, "The New York Scene of 1825", and installed it in one of the rooms of the Academy's present building. It is interesting to consider that all of the objects in this exhibit existed at the time of the organizing of the National Academy.

By 1825, New York's growing population had reached 166,086 and Greenwich was no longer a country village. The city had become the largest and most important one in the country, and its foreign trade nearly equalled half that of the entire nation. DeWitt Clinton was again inaugurated as Governor and later in the year opened the celebrated Erie Canal.

On view in the special room is an impressive oil portrait of Richard A. Striker painted by John Paradise (1783–1833), one of the founders of the National Academy, and a charming view of New York Bay from Staten Island to Sandy Hook executed in 1827 by Thomas Birch, another member of the Academy. Portraits of James and Harriet Augusta (Wetmore) Colles were painted by John Wesley Jarvis in 1822 shortly after their marriage. A watercolor by John Reubens Smith depicts St. George's Church after a fire on January 5th, 1814, which also destroyed many other buildings in the area. Women with buckets helped to fill the engines manned by volunteer firemen. In 1809 an anonymous English merchant visiting New York had described the Church, built in 1749–1752, as "remarkable for bearing as a vane the crown and scepter, said to be the only remains of royalty in the State."

Two colored aquatints of "New York from Weehawk" and "New York from Heights near Brooklyn" portray the city in an exceptionally accurate and beautiful manner. The views, painted by William Guy Wall and engraved by John Hill, were issued in 1823. Also by the same artists are views from the Hudson River Portfolio.

Featured in the center of the gallery is a handsome drum table and two outstanding mahogany side chairs with carved eagle back splats which are thought to have been made about 1810 to 1815 by New York's famous cabinetmaker, Duncan Phyfe. They are part of a set which belonged to DeWitt Clinton and had descended in his family. Although Phyfe did not originate a new furniture style, the quality of his work was outstanding, and he continued to modify his output reflecting the changing tastes of the period. Much of his work was executed in mahogany with detailed, delicate carving of typical ornaments, such as can be seen here. He was one of the first New York cabinetmakers to successfully use the factory method of manufacture, and in later years he employed over a hundred carvers and cabinetmakers. Many prominent New Yorkers were among his customers, including John Jacob Astor.

In the year of the founding of the National Academy of Design, 1825, Phyfe was commissioned to create a gift to be presented to Lafayette as a souvenir of the opening of the Erie Canal. Appropriately, it was a box fitted with glass bottles containing water from the canal. History does not record Lafayette's reaction to this unusual present. However, since he was a Frenchman, we can only hope he didn't sample any of the contents.

Another pair of chairs with splats carved with cornucopias are stamped in the seat frames, "J. L. Stevens", possibly for John Lloyd Stevens, traveler, author and steamship and railroad executive. A mahogany sofa upholstered in red damask with a medallion deeign richly carved with fruit, flowers and leaves is typical of the work done locally in the 1820–1830 decade. Also typical of this period is a secretary labeled by John Van Boskerck at 58 Broad Street. Possibly made by Michael Allison, a contemporary of Duncan Phyfe, is a pair of card tables with lyre supports. Also on exhibit is an arm chair thought to have been made for City Hall, which descended in the family of George Riblet, City Clerk.

Joseph Veach Noble
Director
Museum of the City of New York

President's Medal

The President's Medal was established by Cass Gilbert, NA, the architect for the Woolworth Building, in 1929 under the conditions that it should be awarded at the discretion of the Council of the National Academy to persons who in official positions may have encouraged the development of the fine arts, to great patrons of the arts, to persons who have endowed museums or other institutions for the advancement of the arts, or to artists in any field who have created works of unusual merit. The award may be made to persons in this country or abroad.

This medal has been awarded six times previously:

1929—ELIHU ROOT
1932—*heirs of* SAMUEL FINLEY BREESE MORSE NA
1933—EDWIN H. BLASHFIELD NA
1941—ARCHER M. HUNTINGTON
1963—SIR CHARLES WHEELER, KCVO, *President of the Royal Academy*
1970—LEON KROLL NA

The Honorable Nelson A. Rockefeller, Vice President of the United States, has been elected by the Council of the Academy to be the recipient of the President's Medal for 1975 and has graciously accepted.

The medal was designed by the famous sculptor, Robert Aitken, NA. Its design is simple, with the head of Minerva, Goddess of the Arts on one side, and an arm aiming an arrow at the stars on the other. The only inscription on the award, "Artes ad Astra", means literally "The arts toward the stars."

Above: Obverse.   *Below:* Reverse.

Founders

First Fifteen

CUMMINGS, THOMAS S.
DANFORTH, M. I.
DUNLAP, WILLIAM
DURAND, ASHER B.
FRAZEE, JOHN

INGHAM, CHARLES C.
INMAN, HENRY
MARSIGLIA, G.
MAVERICK, PETER
MORSE, S. F. B.

POTTER, EDWARD C.
REINAGLE, HUGH
TOWN, ITHIEL
WALL, W. G.
WRIGHT, CHARLES C.

Second Fifteen

AGATE, FREDERICK S.
ANDERSON, ALEXANDER
COLE, THOMAS
COYLE, JAMES
EVERS, JOHN

JEWETT, WILLIAM
MAIN, WILLIAM
PARADISE, JOHN
PARISEN, J.
PEALE, REMBRANDT

ROGERS, NATHANIEL
THOMPSON, MARTIN E.
VANDERLYN, JOHN
WALDO, SAMUEL L.
WILSON, D. W.

Presidents

SAMUEL F. B. MORSE	1826—1845	HERBERT ADAMS	1917—1920
ASHER B. DURAND	1845—1861	EDWIN H. BLASHFIELD	1920—1926
SAMUEL F. B. MORSE	1861—1862	CASS GILBERT	1926—1933
DANIEL HUNTINGTON	1862—1870	HARRY W. WATROUS	1933—1934
HENRY P. GRAY	1870—1871	JONAS LIE	1934—1939
WILLIAM PAGE	1871—1873	HOBART NICHOLS	1939—1949
J. Q. A. WARD	1873—1874	DEWITT M. LOCKMAN	1949—1950
WORTHINGTON WHITTREDGE	1874—1877	LAWRENCE GRANT WHITE	1950—1956
DANIEL HUNTINGTON	1877—1890	ELIOT CLARK	1956—1959
THOMAS W. WOOD	1890—1900	JOHN F. HARBESON	1959—1962
FREDERICK DIELMAN	1900—1909	EDGAR I. WILLIAMS	1962—1966
JOHN W. ALEXANDER	1909—1915	ALFRED EASTON POOR	1966—
J. ALDEN WEIR	1915—1917		

Members

Academicians

Painters

	Date Elected		Date Elected
ALBRIGHT, IVAN	1950	FORTESS, KARL E.	1971
ALBRIGHT, MALVIN (ZSISSLY)	1952	GAHMAN, FLOYD	1969
ARONSON, DAVID	1970	GERVASI, FRANK	1960
BECK, MARGIT	1975	GONZALEZ, XAVIER	1955
BETTS, EDWARD	1961	GORSLINE, DOUGLAS	1947
BISHOP, ISABEL	1941	GRABACH, JOHN R.	1968
BOHROD, AARON	1953	GREACEN, NAN	1962
BOSA, LOUIS	1954	GREENE, DANIEL E.	1969
BRACKMAN, ROBERT	1940	GROSHANS, WERNER	1967
BREININ, RAYMOND	1967	HARMON, LILY	1970
BROOK, ALEXANDER	1951	HIRSCH, JOSEPH	1958
BROWNING, COLLEEN	1966	HURD, PETER	1942
CHADBOURN, ALFRED C.	1972	ISENBURGER, ERIC	1957
CHAVEZ, EDWARD	1972	KINSTLER, E. RAYMOND	1974
CIAMPAGLIA, CARLO	1969	KIRSCHENBAUM, JULES	1965
CIKOVSKY, NICOLAI	1970	KOCH, JOHN	1954
CLARK, ELIOT	1944	KONRAD, ADOLF	1970
CLEMENS, PAUL LEWIS	1964	LANING, EDWARD	1958
COINER, CHARLES	1968	LASKER, JOE	1965
COLE, ALPHAEUS P.	1941	LAUFMAN, SIDNEY	1945
COOK, PETER	1966	LEE-SMITH, HUGHIE	1967
COX, ALLYN	1962	LEVINE, DAVID	1971
COX, GARDNER	1970	LOCKE, CHARLES	1951
CURRIE, BRUCE	1970	LUCIONI, LUIGI	1941
DE MARTINI, JOSEPH	1953	MAGAFAN, ETHEL	1968
DICKINSON, EDWIN	1950	MARTIN, FLETCHER	1974
DICKINSON, SIDNEY E.	1927	MARTINO, ANTONIO	1942
DINNERSTEIN, HARVEY	1974	MARTINO, GIOVANNI	1944
DODD, LAMAR	1954	MASON, FRANK	1972
ETNIER, STEPHEN	1953	MAXWELL, JOHN	1975
FARNSWORTH, JERRY	1935	MAYHEW, RICHARD	1971
FLOCH, JOSEPH	1963	MENKES, ZYGMUNT	1964

	Date Elected		Date Elected
MEYEROWITZ, WILLIAM	1959	SERWAZI, ALBERT B.	1971
MOLLER, HANS	1971	SHIKLER, AARON	1965
NELSON, GEORGE L.	1942	SILVERMAN, BURTON	1972
OLINSKY, TOSCA	1969	SLOANE, ERIC	1968
O'TOOLE, CATHAL B.	1944	SOLMAN, JOSEPH	1974
PALMER, WILLIAM	1966	SOYER, RAPHAEL	1951
PARSHALL, DOUGLASS	1969	SPEIGHT, FRANCIS	1940
PHILIPP, ROBERT	1945	TAYLOR, JOHN	1958
PLEISSNER, OGDEN M.	1940	TONEY, ANTHONY	1971
RAY, RUTH	1968	TOOKER, GEORGE	1970
ROBERTS, PRISCILLA	1957	TREBILCOCK, PAUL	1964
ROMANO, UMBERTO	1957	VICKREY, ROBERT	1964
RYERSON, MARGERY	1959	WARREN, FERDINAND E.	1948
SAMSTAG, GORDON	1965	WHITE, CHARLES	1974
SAVAGE, EUGENE	1926	WILLIAMS, J. SCOTT	1938
SAWYER, HELEN	1950	WRIGHT, CATHARINE M.	1969
SCHLAIKJER, JES	1948	ZIMMERMAN, PAUL W.	1972

Sculptors

	Date Elected		Date Elected
AMATEIS, EDMOND R.	1942	FRUDAKIS, EVANGELOS	1964
BELSKIE, ABRAM	1965	GRUPPE, KARL H.	1950
BLOCK, ADOLPH	1967	HANCOCK, WALKER	1939
CARTER, GRANVILLE W.	1964	HARDIN, ADLAI S.	1963
CECERE, GAETANO	1938	HARTWIG, CLEO	1971
DE COUX, JANET	1967	JACKSON, HAZEL BRILL	1961
DE CREEFT, JOSE	1964	JENNEWEIN, C. PAUL	1933
DE LUE, DONALD	1943	JUDSON, SYLVIA SHAW	1965
DE MARCO, JEAN	1966	KISELEWSKI, JOSEPH	1944
ELISCU, FRANK	1967	LANTZ, MICHAEL	1954
FASANO, CLARA	1968	LATHROP, GERTRUDE	1940
FJELDE, PAUL	1957	LO MEDICO, THOMAS	1969
FREDERICKS, MARSHALL	1961	MANCA, ALBINO	1966
FRISHMUTH, HARRIET	1929	MANKOWSKI, BRUNO	1968

	Date Elected		Date Elected
MARANS, MOISSAYE	1971	RUDY, CHARLES	1967
MELLON, ELEANOR M.	1950	SANFORD, MARION	1963
MONTANA, PIETRO	1970	SNOWDEN, GEORGE	1941
MOORE, BRUCE	1942	WARNEKE, HEINZ	1966
NICKERSON, RUTH	1966	WEEMS, KATHARINE LANE	1939
PUTNAM, BRENDA	1936	WEINMAN, ROBERT A.	1973
RECCHIA, RICHARD	1944	WINKEL, NINA	1973

Architects

	Date Elected		Date Elected
ABRAMOVITZ, MAX	1974	KILHAM, WALTER H., JR.	1958
BARNES, EDWARD L.	1974	KIMBALL, RICHARD	1961
BELLUSCHI, PIETRO	1957	OWINGS, NATHANIEL A.	1967
BUNSHAFT, GORDON	1959	PEI, I. M.	1965
CLARKE, GILMORE D.	1946	PLATT, WILLIAM	1948
FULLER, R. BUCKMINSTER	1970	POOR, ALFRED EASTON	1963
HARBESON, JOHN F.	1957	RAPUANO, MICHAEL	1959
HARRISON, WALLACE K.	1948	ROCHE, KEVIN	1973
HUTCHINS, ROBERT S.	1970	STONE, EDWARD D.	1956
JOHNSON, PHILIP C.	1963	STUBBINS, HUGH A.	1974
KEALLY, FRANCIS	1967	THIRY, PAUL	1967

Workers in the Graphic Arts

	Date Elected		Date Elected
ALBEE, GRACE	1946	NOBLE, JOHN A.	1969
BRUSSEL–SMITH, BERNARD	1973	PARTRIDGE, ROI	1949
COOK, HOWARD N.	1949	REED, DOEL	1952
CSOKA, STEPHEN	1948	ROSENBERG, LOUIS C.	1936
EICHENBERG, FRITZ	1949	RUZICKA, RUDOLPH	1966
JELINEK, HANS	1968	TURNER, JANET E.	1974
KLOSS, GENE	1972	WARD, LYND	1958
LANDECK, ARMIN	1942	WEIDENAAR, REYNOLD H.	1965
LEIGHTON, CLARE	1949	WENGENROTH, STOW	1941
LOGGIE, HELEN	1971	WINKLER, JOHN W.	1943
MEISSNER, LEO	1969		

Aquarellists

	Date Elected		Date Elected
ASPLUND, TORE	1951	MCCOY, JOHN W., II	1950
BRANDT, REXFORD	1974	NICHOLAS, THOMAS	1970
CHEN CHI	1964	PELLEW, JOHN C.	1952
COOPER, MARIO	1952	PIKE, JOHN	1948
DIKE, PHILIP L.	1953	PITZ, HENRY C.	1969
GASSER, HENRY	1950	SCHWEITZER, GERTRUDE	1951
GRAMATKY, HARDIE	1950	SHEETS, MILLARD	1947
HELCK, PETER	1950	SMITH, WILLIAM A.	1952
JAMISON, PHILIP	1970	TEAGUE, DONALD	1948
KINGHAN, CHARLES R.	1971	THON, WILLIAM	1968
KINGMAN, DONG	1951	WHITAKER, FREDERIC	1951
LOGAN, MAURICE	1960	WYETH, ANDREW	1945

Associates

Painters

	Date Elected		Date Elected
APT, CHARLES	1972	PENNEY, JAMES	1972
BLUME, PETER	1948	POOR, ANNE	1972
DOBBS, JOHN	1973	PRESTOPINO, GREGORIO	1973
GWATHMEY, ROBERT	1973	REFREGIER, ANTON	1969
HENDERSON, JACK	1972	ROSE, HERMAN	1974
KAMIHIRA, BEN	1959	STODDARD, ALICE KENT	1938
KEPES, GYORGY	1973	WICKWIRE, JERE	1936
KOERNER, HENRY	1965	WILES, GLADYS	1934
LEVI, JULIAN	1973	WILSON, JANE	1974

Sculptors

	Date Elected		Date Elected
AGOPOFF, AGOP	1969	CHANDLER, ELISABETH GORDON	1973
BARBAROSSA, THEODORE C.	1971	DUNWIDDIE, CHARLOTTE	1969

	Date Elected		Date Elected
DU PEN, EVERETT G.	1971	LUCCHESI, BRUNO	1965
HOFFMAN, EDWARD FENNO, III	1969	MORENON, ERNEST	1971
HORN, MILTON	1973	SALERNO, CHARLES	1970
HUMES, RALPH	1969	WEIN, ALBERT	1974
JONES, DEXTER	1967	WU, LINDA	1969

Architects

	Date Elected		Date Elected
ANDERSON, LAWRENCE B.	1965	KILEY, DANIEL	1963
AYERS, RICHARD W.	1969	KLING, VINCENT GEORGE	1964
BASSETT, EDWARD C.	1970	LA FARGE, LOUIS BANCEL	1960
BEVIN, NEWTON P.	1964	LAWFORD, GEOFFRY N.	1960
BORN, ERNEST A.	1973	MEEM, JOHN GAW	1942
CAIN, WALKER O.	1962	MOORE, JOHN CROSBY BROWN	1957
CAVAGLIERI, GIORGIO	1970	NOYES, ELIOT F.	1967
COIT, ELISABETH	1973	O'CONNOR, ROBERT B.	1953
DU BOSE, CHARLES	1972	PLATT, GEOFFREY	1975
ECKBO, GARRETT	1964	QUALLS, GEORGE W.	1972
EGGERS, DAVID L.	1972	RICH, LORIMER	1968
FAULKNER, WALDRON	1965	RUSSELL, GEORGE V.	1972
FLETCHER, NORMAN C.	1970	SASAKI, HIDEO	1968
GEDDES, ROBERT L.	1967	SCHMIDT, MOTT B.	1972
GOLDSTONE, HARMON H.	1971	SHERWOOD, THORNE	1961
GRISWOLD, RALPH E.	1960	SHURCLIFF, SIDNEY N.	1970
HARBESON, PAUL CRET	1974	SIMONDS, JOHN O.	1969
HARKNESS, ALBERT	1951	SIMONS, ALBERT	1955
HARKNESS, JOHN C.	1971	SMITH, CHLOETHIEL WOODWARD	1973
HOFFMAN, F. BURRALL	1958	SWANKE, ALBERT H.	1969
HOMSEY, SAMUEL E.	1962	TAFEL, EDGAR A.	1971
IVES, PHILIP	1971	WARNECKE, JOHN CARL	1958
JOHANSEN, JOHN M.	1969	WEBEL, RICHARD K.	1963
KENNEDY, EUGENE F., JR.	1962	WEESE, HARRY MOHR	1965
KETCHUM, MORRIS, JR.	1962	YOUNG, THEODORE J.	1970

Workers in the Graphic Arts

	Date Elected		Date Elected
BACON, PEGGY	1947	LANDAU, JACOB	1974
BOYD, FISKE	1948	LATHROP, DOROTHY P.	1949
COUGHLIN, JACK	1972	LIBBY, WILLIAM CHARLES	1969
DE POL, JOHN	1954	MENIHAN, JOHN C.	1948
EAMES, JOHN HEAGAN	1953	MUENCH, JOHN	1972
FLORSHEIM, RICHARD	1968	PHILBRICK, MARGARET	1970
FRASCONI, ANTONIO	1962	ROMANO, CLARE	1970
GANNETT, RUTH	1969	ROSS, JOHN	1970
GEYER, HAROLD C.	1950	TAYLOR, PRENTISS	1948
HECHENBLEIKNER, LOUIS	1961	UNWIN, NORA S.	1953
JONYNAS, VYTAUTAS K.	1973	VON NEUMANN, ROBERT	1954
KAPPEL, PHILIP	1967	WATERS, HERBERT	1955
KUPFERMAN, LAWRENCE	1943		

Aquarellists

	Date Elected		Date Elected
ANDERSON, HARRY	1965	HOOK, WALTER	1972
AVERY, RALPH	1956	JOHNSON, AVERY	1965
BALLINGER, HARRY RUSSELL	1965	JONES, CAROL PYLE	1974
BONGART, SERGEI	1968	KAEP, LOUIS J.	1956
BOWES, BETTY M.	1975	KESTER, LENARD	1958
BROWNE, SYD	1951	KLEBE, GENE	1969
CARTER, CLARENCE	1949	LAESSIG, ROBERT H.	1964
CHIARA, ALAN R.	1970	MAC NUTT, GLENN GORDON	1956
COES, KENT DAY	1963	MEYERS, DALE	1972
DAHLBERG, EDWIN L.	1973	PARADISE, PHIL	1953
DE KNIGHT, AVEL	1966	RICCI, JERRI	1951
FITZGERALD, EDMOND J.	1962	RICHARDS, WALTER DU BOIS	1974
GIBSON, GEORGE	1956	ROSS, ALEX	1965
GROTH, JOHN	1958	SANTORO, JOSEPH L. C.	1971
GUMPEL, HUGH	1961	SETTERBERG, CARL	1962
GUTE, HERBERT J.	1961	STONE, DON	1968
HILL, TOM	1974	STRISIK, PAUL	1971
HOLLERBACH, SERGE	1973	STROSAHL, WILLIAM	1972

	Date Elected		Date Elected
WALLEEN, HANS AXEL	1969	WHITAKER, EILEEN MONAGHAN	1957
WEBSTER, LARRY	1974	WHITNEY, EDGAR A.	1971
WENTWORTH, MURRAY	1972	WOOD, ROBERT E.	1971
WHEAT, JOHN POTTER	1957	ZORNES, MILFORD	1964

Elects

Academicians

Painters

BLUME, PETER
GWATHMEY, ROBERT
KAMIHIRA, BEN
KOERNER, HENRY
PENNEY, JAMES
POOR, ANNE
REFREIGIER, ANTON

STODDARD, ALICE KENT
WICKWIRE, JERE

Sculptors
LUCCHESI, BRUNO

Architects
CAIN, WALKER O.
WEESE, HARRY M.

Workers in the Graphic Arts
BACON, PEGGY
FRASCONI, ANTONIO

Aquarellists
DE KNIGHT, AVEL

Associates

Painters

BARNET, WILL
BISCHOFF, ELMER
BROCKHURST, GERALD
CALLAHAN, KENNETH
ESTES, RICHARD
GILLESPIE, GREGORY
GREENE, BALCOMB
GROPPER, WILLIAM
GUERIN, JOHN
LAWRENCE, JACOB
LESLIE, ALFRED
PERLIN, BERNARD
PRICE, ALAN
RATTNER, ABRAHAM
REID, CHARLES

TAM, REUBEN
TOBEY, MARK
WYETH, HENRIETTE
WYETH, JAMES

Sculptors
BROWN, JOSEPH
BUNN, KENNETH RODNEY
GIBRAN, KAHLIL
PARKS, CHARLES C.
PARKS, CHRISTOPHER

Architects
BALLARD, WILLIAM F. R.
BOWER, JOHN ARNOLD, JR.
FORD, O'NEIL
LABATUT, JEAN

MITCHELL, EHRMAN BURKMAN, JR.
NETSCH, WALTER A.
NICHOLS, FREDERICK DOVETON
THOMPSON, BENJAMIN
TYNG, ANNE GRISWOLD
ZION, ROBERT L.

Workers in the Graphic Arts
DOMJAN, JOSEPH
KOHN, MISCH
MILTON, PETER
PETERDI, GABOR

Aquarellists
BYE, RANULPH DE BAYEUX
COBB, RUTH
WHITE, DORIS

Deceased Academicians

(* Also a member of the Society of American Artists. † Founder National Academy of Design.)

Painters

	Elected	Died		Elected	Died
ABBEY, EDWIN A.*	1902	1911	BLAUVELT, CHAS. F.*	1859	1900
ADAMS, KENNETH M.	1961	1966	BLUM, ROBT. F.*	1893	1903
ADAMS, WAYMAN	1926	1959	BLUMENSCHEIN, ERNEST L.	1927	1960
AGATE, FRED S.†	1826	1844	BOGLE, JAMES	1861	1873
ALEXANDER, J. W.*	1902	1915	BOHM, MAX	1920	1923
ALLEN, CHARLES C.	1945	1950	BORIE, ADOLPHE	1934	1934
ALLEN, JUNIUS	1941	1962	BOUCHE, LOUIS	1950	1969
AMES, JOSEPH	1870	1872	BOUGHTON, G. H.	1871	1905
ANDERSON, KARL	1923	1956	BOWER, ALEXANDER	1950	1952
AUDUBON, V. G.	1846	1860	BRANDT, CARL L.	1872	1905
AUERBACH-LEVY, WM.	1958	1964	BREVOORT, JAS. R.	1863	1918
BAKER, GEORGE A.	1851	1880	BRIDGMAN, F. A.*	1881	1928
BALLIN, HUGO	1940	1956	BRISTOL, JOHN B.	1875	1909
BARSE, G. R., JR.*	1900	1938	BROWN, J. G.	1863	1913
BATES, KENNETH	1960	1973	BROWN, ROY	1926	1956
BEAL, GIFFORD	1914	1956	BROWNE, GEO. E.	1928	1946
BEARD, JAMES H.	1872	1893	BRUSH, G. DE F.*	1908	1941
BEARD, WM. H.	1862	1900	BUNCE, WM. G.*	1907	1916
BEAUX, CECILIA*	1902	1942	BURROUGHS, B.*	1930	1934
BECKWITH, J. C.*	1894	1917	BUTLER, GEO. B.*	1873	1907
BELCHER, HILDA	1932	1963	BUTLER, H. R.*	1900	1934
BELLOWS, A. F.	1861	1883	CAFFERTY, J. H.	1853	1869
BELLOWS, GEORGE W.	1913	1925	CARLSEN, DINES	1941	1966
BENNETT, WM. J.	1828	1844	CARLSEN, EMIL*	1906	1932
BENSON, FRANK W.*	1905	1951	CARLSON, JOHN F.	1925	1945
BENTON, THOMAS HART	1956	1975	CARROLL, JOHN	1950	1959
BERMAN, EUGENE	1954	1972	CASILEAR, JOHN W.	1851	1893
BETTS, LOUIS	1915	1961	CHAPIN, FRANCIS	1953	1965
BIERSTADT, ALBERT	1860	1902	CHAPMAN, CHAS. S.	1926	1962
BITTINGER, CHARLES	1937	1970	CHAPMAN, C. T.*	1914	1925
BLAKELOCK, R. A.	1916	1919	CHAPMAN, J. G.	1836	1889
BLASHFIELD, E. H.*	1888	1936	CHASE, WM. M.*	1890	1916

	Elected	Died		Elected	Died
CHURCH, FRED E.	1849	1900	DEWEY, CHAS. M.*	1907	1937
CHURCH, F. S.*	1885	1924	DEWING, T. W.*	1888	1938
CLARK, WALTER*	1909	1917	DIELMAN, FRED*	1883	1935
CLINEDINST, B. W.*	1898	1931	DOBKIN, ALEXANDER	1973	1975
COFFIN, WM. A.*	1912	1925	DOLPH, J. H.*	1898	1903
COLE, THOMAS†	1826	1848	DOUGHERTY, PAUL*	1907	1947
COLMAN, SAMUEL*	1862	1920	DU BOIS, GUY PENE	1940	1958
CONNAWAY, JAY	1943	1970	DUFNER, EDWARD	1929	1957
COOPER, COLIN C.	1912	1937	DUGGAN, PETER P.	1851	1861
CORBINO, JON	1940	1964	DUMOND, FRANK V.*	1906	1951
CORNWELL, DEAN	1940	1960	DUNLAP, WILLIAM†	1826	1839
COSTIGAN, JOHN E.	1928	1972	DUNN, HARVEY	1945	1952
COUSE, E. I.	1911	1936	DURAND, ASHER B.†	1826	1886
COVEY, ARTHUR S.	1934	1960	DUVENECK, FRANK*	1906	1919
COX, KENYON*	1903	1919	EAKINS, THOMAS*	1902	1916
COYLE, JAMES†	1826	1828	EDMONDS, F. W.	1840	1863
CRANCH, C. P.	1864	1892	EDWARDS, G. W.	1945	1950
CRANE, BRUCE*	1901	1937	EHNINGER, J. W.	1860	1889
CRISP, ARTHUR	1937	1974	ELLIOTT, CHAS. L.	1846	1868
CROPSEY, J. F.	1851	1900	EMMET, LYDIA F.	1912	1952
CUMMINGS, T. S.†	1826	1894	EVERS, JOHN†	1826	1884
CUMMINGS, WILLARD	1969	1975	FARNDON, WALTER	1937	1964
CURRAN, CHAS. C.*	1904	1942	FAULKNER, BARRY	1931	1966
CURRY, JOHN S.	1943	1946	FIENE, ERNEST	1952	1965
DABO, LEON	1944	1960	FISHER, ANNA	1932	1942
DAINGERFIELD, E.*	1906	1932	FISKE, GERTRUDE	1930	1961
DANA, W. P. W..	1863	1927	FLAGG, GEO. W.	1851	1897
DAVEY, RANDALL	1938	1964	FLAGG, JARED	1849	1899
DAVIS, CHAS. H.*	1906	1933	FLAGG, MONTAGUE*	1910	1915
DAVIS, GLADYS R.	1943	1967	FOLINSBEE, JOHN F.	1928	1972
DEARTH, H. G.*	1906	1918	FOSTER, BEN*	1904	1926
DE FOREST, L.	1898	1932	FOWLER, FRANK*	1900	1910
DE HAAS, M. F. H.	1867	1895	FRANZEN, AUGUST*	1920	1938
DE HAVEN, B. F.	1920	1934	FREEMAN, JAS. E.	1833	1884
DE ROSE, A. L.	1833	1836	FRIESEKE, FRED K.	1914	1939
DESSAR, LOUIS P.*	1906	1952	FROTHINGHAM, JAS.	1831	1864

	Elected	Died		Elected	Died
GARBER, DANIEL	1913	1958	HICKS, THOMAS	1851	1890
GAUL, GILBERT*	1882	1919	HIGGINS, EUGENE	1928	1958
GAY, EDWARD	1907	1928	HIGGINS, VICTOR	1935	1949
GIFFORD, R. SWAIN*	1878	1905	HILDEBRANDT, H.	1932	1958
GIFFORD, S. R.	1854	1880	HOMER, WINSLOW	1865	1910
GIGNOUX, REGIS F.	1851	1882	HOPKINSON, CHARLES	1929	1962
GILES, HOWARD E.	1929	1955	HOVENDEN, THOS.*	1882	1895
GLACKENS, WM. J.*	1933	1938	HOWE, WM. H.*	1897	1929
GRANVILLE-SMITH, W.	1915	1938	HOWLAND, ALF. C.	1882	1909
GRAY, HENRY P.	1842	1877	HOYLE, RAPHAEL	1831	1836
GREACEN, EDMUND	1935	1949	HUBBARD, R. W.	1858	1888
GREENE, E. D. E.	1858	1879	HUNTINGTON, DANIEL	1840	1906
GREENWOOD, MARION	1959	1970	HUTCHISON, F. W.	1935	1953
GRIFFIN, WALTER	1922	1935	INGHAM, CHAS. C.†	1826	1863
GRISWOLD, C. C.	1867	1918	INMAN, HENRY†	1826	1846
GROLL, ALBERT L.	1910	1952	INNESS, GEORGE*	1868	1894
GUERIN, JULES	1931	1946	INNESS, GEO., JR.*	1899	1926
GUY, SEYMOUR J.	1865	1910	IPSEN, ERNEST L.	1924	1951
HALE, LILIAN W.	1931	1963	IRVING, J. B.	1872	1877
HALL, MISS ANN	1833	1863	ISHAM, SAMUEL*	1906	1914
HALL, GEO. HENRY	1868	1913	JEWETT, WILLIAM†	1826	1874
HAMILTON, H.	1889	1928	JOCELYN, N.	1846	1881
HANSEN, ARMIN C.	1948	1957	JOHANSEN, JOHN C.	1915	1964
HARDING, GEORGE	1945	1959	JOHNSON, DAVID	1861	1908
HARRISON, ALEX*	1901	1930	JOHNSON, EASTMAN*	1860	1906
HARRISON, BIRGE*	1910	1929	JOHNSON, F. T.	1937	1939
HART, JAMES M.	1859	1901	JONES, FRANCIS C.*	1894	1932
HART, WILLIAM	1858	1894	JONES, H. BOLTON*	1883	1927
HASELTINE, W. S.	1861	1900	KENDALL, SERGEANT*	1905	1938
HASSAM, CHILDE*	1906	1935	KENSETT, J. F.	1849	1872
HAWTHORNE, C. W.	1911	1930	KING, PAUL	1933	1947
HENNESSY, W. J.	1863	1917	KNATHS, KARL	1971	1971
HENRI, ROBERT*	1906	1929	KOST, F. W.*	1906	1923
HENRY, EDW. L.	1869	1919	KROLL, LEON	1927	1974
HERTER, ALBERT*	1943	1950	KRONBERG, LOUIS	1943	1965
HIBBARD, ALDRO T.	1933	1972	LA FARGE, JOHN*	1869	1910

	Elected	Died		Elected	Died
LAMBDIN, G. C.	1868	1896	MILLER, CHAS. H.*	1875	1922
LANG, LOUIS	1852	1893	MILLER, KENNETH H.	1944	1952
LASCARI, SALVATORE	1945	1967	MILLER, RICHARD E.	1915	1943
LATHROP, W. L.	1907	1938	MILLET, FRANCIS D.*	1885	1912
LAWSON, ERNEST	1917	1939	MINOR, ROBERT C.*	1897	1904
LEBRUN, RICO	1963	1964	MIXTER, FELICIE HOWELL	1945	1968
LE CLEAR, THOS.	1863	1882	MOELLER, LOUIS	1895	1930
LEIGH, WILLIAM R.	1955	1955	MOFFETT, ROSS	1942	1971
LEITH-ROSS, HARRY	1936	1973	MOONEY, EDWARD	1840	1887
LEUTZE, E.	1860	1868	MORA, F. LUIS*	1906	1940
LEVER, HAYLEY	1933	1958	MORAN, THOMAS*	1884	1926
LIBERTE, JEAN	1960	1965	MORSE, S. F. B.†	1826	1872
LIE, JONAS	1925	1940	MORTON, JOHN L.	1831	1871
LIPPINCOTT, W. H.	1897	1920	MOUNT, S. A.	1842	1868
LOCKMAN, DE WITT	1921	1957	MOUNT, WM. S.	1832	1868
LOCKWOOD, R. W.*	1912	1914	MOWBRAY, H. S.*	1891	1928
LOEB, LOUIS*	1906	1909	MURPHY, H. D.	1934	1945
LOOP, HENRY A.	1861	1895	MURPHY, J. F.*	1887	1921
LOW, WILL H.*	1890	1932	MYERS, JEROME	1929	1940
LUCAS, ALBERT P.	1927	1945	NEHLIG, VICTOR	1870	1909
MAC LANE, JEAN	1926	1964	NEILSON, RAYMOND P. R.	1938	1964
MAC RAE, EMMA FORDYCE	1951	1974	NEWELL, G. GLENN	1937	1947
MAGRATH, WM.	1876	1918	NICHOLS, HOBART	1920	1962
MARSH, REGINALD	1943	1954	NICHOLS, SPENCER	1933	1950
MARSIGLIA, G.†	1826	1850	NICOLL, JAMES C.	1885	1918
MARTIN, H. D.*	1874	1897	NISBET, ROBERT	1928	1961
MASON, ROY	1940	1972	NOBLE, JOHN	1927	1934
MATTSON, HENRY E.	1951	1971	OAKLEY, VIOLET	1929	1961
MAYER, HENRIK MARTIN	1969	1972	OBERTEUFFER, GEO.	1938	1940
MAYNARD, G. W.*	1885	1923	OCHTMAN, DOROTHY	1971	1971
MAYR, C.	1849	1850	OCHTMAN, L.*	1904	1934
MC ENTEE, JERVIS	1861	1891	OLINSKY, IVAN G.	1919	1962
MC FEE, HENRY LEE	1950	1953	PAGE, WILLIAM	1836	1885
MELCHERS, GARI*	1906	1932	PALMER, WALTER*	1897	1932
MEYER, HERBERT	1942	1960	PARADISE, JOHN†	1826	1833
MIGNOT, LOUIS R.	1859	1870	PARISEN, J.†	1826	1833

	Elected	Died		Elected	Died
PARRISH, MAXFIELD*	1906	1966	ROGERS, NATHANIEL†	1826	1844
PARSHALL, DE WITT	1917	1956	ROOK, EDWARD F.	1924	1960
PARTON, ARTHUR	1884	1914	ROSEN, CHARLES	1917	1950
PARTON, H. W.	1929	1933	ROSSITER, THOS. P.	1849	1871
PAXTON, WM. M.	1928	1941	ROTH, ERNEST D.	1928	1964
PEALE, REMBRANDT†	1826	1860	RUNGIUS, CARL	1920	1959
PEARSON, J. T., JR.	1919	1951	RYDER, ALBERT P.*	1906	1917
PERRINE, VAN DEARING	1931	1955	RYDER, C. F.	1920	1949
PERRY, E. WOOD	1869	1915	SAMPLE, PAUL	1941	1974
PITTMAN, HOBSON	1953	1972	SARGENT, JOHN S.*	1897	1925
POND, DANA	1945	1962	SCHOFIELD, W. E.*	1907	1944
POOLE, ABRAM	1938	1961	SELLSTED, LARS G.	1874	1911
POOR, HENRY V.	1963	1970	SEPESHY, ZOLTAN	1945	1948
PORTER, BENJ. C.*	1880	1908	SEYFFERT, LEOPOLD	1925	1956
POTTER, EDW. C.†	1826	1826	SHATTUCK, A. D.	1861	1928
POTTHAST, EDW. H.*	1906	1927	SHEGOGUE, JAS. H.	1843	1872
POWELL, A. J. E.	1937	1956	SHINN, EVERETT	1943	1953
PRATT, R. M.	1851	1880	SHIRLAW, WALTER*	1888	1909
PRELLWITZ, HENRY*	1912	1940	SHUMWAY, H. C.	1832	1884
PYLE, HOWARD	1907	1911	SHURTLEFF, R. M.	1890	1915
QUARTLEY, ARTHUR*	1886	1886	SINGER, W. H., JR.	1931	1943
RANGER, H. W.	1906	1916	SMEDLEY, WM. T.*	1905	1920
REDFIELD, ED. W.*	1906	1965	SMILLIE, GEO. H.	1882	1921
REHN, F. K. M.*	1908	1914	SMILLIE, JAS. D.	1876	1909
REID, ROBERT*	1906	1929	SMITH, HOWARD E.	1969	1970
REINAGLE, HUGH†	1826	1834	SNELL, HENRY B.*	1906	1943
RICHARDS, T. A.	1851	1900	SONNTAG, WM. L.	1861	1900
RICHARDS, W. T.	1871	1905	SOYER, MOSES	1966	1974
RICHARDSON, A.	1833	1876	SPEICHER, EUGENE	1925	1962
RITCHIE, ALEX. H.	1871	1895	SPENCER, F. R.	1846	1875
RITMAN, LOUIS	1950	1963	SPENCER, ROBERT	1920	1931
RITSCHEL, WILLIAM	1914	1949	STAIGG, RICH. M.	1861	1881
RITTENBERG, HENRY R.	1927	1969	STEARNS, J. B.	1849	1885
ROBBINS, H. W.	1878	1904	STERNE, MAURICE	1944	1957
ROBERTS, MORTON	1958	1964	STERNER, ALBERT	1934	1946
ROBINSON, W. S.	1911	1945	STEVENS, W. LESTER	1943	1969

	Elected	Died		Elected	Died
STONE, WM. O.	1859	1875	WALL, WM. G.†	1826	1864
STUEMPFIG, WALTER	1953	1970	WARD, EDGAR M.	1883	1915
SUYDAM, JAS. A.	1861	1865	WARNER, EVERETT	1937	1963
SYMONS, G. G.	1911	1930	WATKINS, FRANKLIN	1957	1972
TAIT, ARTHUR F.	1858	1905	WATROUS, H. W.*	1895	1940
TANNER, HENRY O.	1927	1937	WAUGH, FRED J.	1911	1940
TARBELL, E. C.*	1906	1938	WEIR, J. ALDEN*	1886	1919
THAYER, ABBOTT H.*	1901	1921	WEIR, JOHN F.	1866	1926
THOMPSON, A. W.*	1875	1896	WEIR, ROBT. W.	1829	1889
THOMPSON, L. P.	1937	1963	WELDON, CHAS. D.	1897	1935
THORNE, WILLIAM*	1913	1956	WENZLER, H. A.	1860	1871
TIFFANY, LOUIS C.*	1880	1933	WESCOTT, PAUL	1970	1970
TRYON, D. W.*	1891	1925	WHITE, EDWIN	1849	1877
TURNER, CHAS. Y.*	1886	1918	WHITEHORNE, JAS.	1833	1888
TURNER, HELEN M.	1921	1958	WHITTREDGE, W.	1861	1910
TWIBILL, GEO. W.	1833	1836	WIGGINS, GUY	1935	1962
TYSON, CARROLL S.	1944	1956	WIGGINS, J. C.*	1906	1932
UFER, WALTER	1926	1936	WILES, IRVING R.*	1897	1948
V. BOSKERCK, R. W.*	1907	1932	WILLIAMS, F. B.	1909	1956
VANDERLYN, J.†	1826	1852	WILLIAMS, K. S.	1942	1951
VAN ELTEN, K.	1883	1904	WILMARTH, L. E.	1873	1918
VAN LAER, A. T.	1909	1920	WILSON, D. W.†	1826	1827
VAN SOELEN, THEODORE	1940	1964	WILSON, SOL	1970	1974
VEDDER, ELIHU*	1865	1923	WINTER, ANDREW	1938	1958
VER BRYCK, C.	1841	1844	WINTER, EZRA	1928	1949
VINTON, FRED P.*	1891	1911	WOOD, THOS. W.	1871	1903
VOLK, DOUGLAS*	1899	1935	WOODBURY, C. H.*	1907	1940
VONNOH, ROBT. W.*	1906	1933	WYANT, ALEX H.*	1869	1892
WALDO, S. L.†	1826	1861	WYETH, N. C.	1941	1945
WALKER, H. O.*	1902	1929	YATES, CULLEN	1919	1945
WALKER, HORATIO	1891	1938	YEWELL, GEO. H.	1880	1923

Sculptors

	Elected	Died		Elected	Died
ADAMS, HERBERT*	1899	1945	HASELTINE, HERBERT	1946	1962
AITKEN, ROBERT	1914	1949	HERING, HENRY	1937	1949
ANGEL, JOHN	1948	1960	HINTON, CHARLES L.	1941	1950
BAKER, BRYANT	1959	1970	HOFFMAN, MALVINA	1931	1966
BARTLETT, PAUL W.*	1917	1925	HORD, DONAL	1951	1966
BEACH, CHESTER	1924	1956	HOWARD, CECIL	1948	1956
BITTER, KARL T. F.*	1903	1915	HUNTINGTON, ANNA HYATT	1922	1973
BROS, ROBERT	1968	1969	JONES, THOMAS H.	1968	1969
BROWN, HENRY K.	1851	1886	KECK, CHARLES	1928	1951
CALDER, A. STIRLING*	1913	1945	KEYES, BESSIE P. V.*	1921	1955
CALVERLY, CHARLES	1874	1914	KONTI, ISIDORE	1909	1938
CHAPIN, CORNELIA VAN A.	1945	1972	KORBEL, MARIO	1944	1954
CHOATE, NATHANIEL	1955	1965	KREIS, HENRY	1951	1963
CRESSON, MARGARET FRENCH	1959	1973	LAESSLE, ALBERT	1932	1954
DALLIN, CYRUS E.	1930	1944	LAUNITZ, R. E.	1833	1870
DALTON, PETER	1952	1972	LAWRIE, LEE	1932	1963
DE FRANCISCI, ANTHONY	1937	1964	LENTELLI, LEO	1943	1961
DEMETRIOS, GEORGE	1963	1974	LOBER, GEORG	1935	1961
DERUJINSKY, GLEB W.	1953	1975	LONGMAN, EVELYN	1919	1954
DUBLE, LU	1967	1970	LOVET-LORSKI, BORIS	1960	1973
ELLERHUSEN, ULRIC H.	1934	1957	MAC MONNIES, F. W.*	1906	1937
EVANS, RUDULPH	1929	1960	MAC NEIL, H. A.*	1906	1947
FLANAGAN, JOHN	1928	1952	MANSHIP, PAUL	1916	1966
FRASER, J. E.	1917	1953	MC CARTAN, EDWARD	1925	1947
FRASER, LAURA GARDIN	1931	1966	MESTROVIC, IVAN	1956	1962
FRAZEE, JOHN†	1826	1852	MILLES, CARL.	1953	1955
FRENCH, DANIEL C.*	1901	1931	NEBEL, BERTHOLD	1946	1964
FRIEDLANDER, LEO	1949	1966	NIEHAUS, C. H.	1906	1935
FRY, SHERRY E.	1930	1966	PICCIRILLI, ATTILIO	1935	1945
GLINSKY, VINCENT	1970	1975	PICCIRILLI, FURIO	1936	1949
GRAFLY, CHARLES*	1905	1929	PLATT, ELEANOR	1963	1974
GREGORY, JOHN	1934	1958	POLASEK, ALBIN	1933	1965
GRIMES, FRANCES	1945	1963	POTTER, EDW. C.*	1906	1923
HARTLEY, J. SCOTT*	1891	1912	PROCTOR, A. P.*	1904	1950

	Elected	Died		Elected	Died
QUATTROCCHI, EDMONDO	1956	1966	STEWART, ALBERT	1945	1965
RENIER, JOSEPH	1955	1966	TAFT, LORADO	1911	1936
ROGERS, JOHN	1863	1904	THOMPSON, LAUNT	1862	1894
ROTH, FRED G. R.*	1906	1944	WARD, J. Q. A.	1863	1910
ROX, HENRY	1965	1967	WARNER, OLIN L.*	1889	1896
SAINT-GAUDENS, A.*	1889	1907	WAUGH, SIDNEY	1938	1963
SALVATORE, VICTOR	1957	1965	WEINMAN, A. A.*	1911	1952
SCHMITZ, CARL L.	1955	1967	WILLIAMS, WHEELER	1940	1972
SPRINGWEILER, ERWIN	1967	1968	YOUNG, MAHONRI	1923	1957

Architects

	Elected	Died		Elected	Died
ALDRICH, CHESTER	1939	1940	HASTINGS, THOMAS	1909	1929
ALDRICH, WILLIAM T.	1944	1966	HEPBURN, ANDREW H.	1962	1967
ATTERBURY, G.	1940	1956	HEWITT, EDWARD S.	1948	1962
AYRES, LOUIS	1936	1947	HEWLETT, J. M.	1931	1941
BACON, HENRY	1917	1924	HOLABIRD, JOHN	1944	1945
BOSWORTH, WELLES	1928	1966	KENDALL, WM. M.	1935	1941
BROWN, ARCH. M.	1953	1956	KING, FREDERIC R.	1955	1972
BROWN, ARTHUR, JR.	1953	1957	LA BEAUME, LOUIS	1949	1961
BRUNNER, A. W.	1916	1925	LAMB, W. F.	1950	1952
CARRERE, JOHN M.	1910	1911	LARSON, ROY F.	1963	1973
COOK, WALTER	1912	1916	LAY, CHARLES D.	1948	1956
CORBETT, HARVEY W.	1930	1954	LINDEBERG, H. T.	1949	1959
CRET, PAUL P.	1938	1945	MAGINNIS, CHAS. D.	1942	1955
DELANO, WM. A.	1937	1960	MC KIM, CHAS. F.	1907	1909
EGGERS, OTTO R.	1951	1964	MEAD, W. R.	1910	1928
ELLETT, THOMAS H.	1945	1951	MEEKS, EVERETT	1949	1954
FERRISS, HUGH	1960	1962	MIES, VAN DER ROHE	1964	1969
FREEDLANDER, J. H.	1932	1943	MORRIS, BENJ. W.	1941	1944
GILBERT, CASS	1908	1934	OLMSTED, FRED. LAW	1929	1957
GOODHUE, B.	1923	1924	ORR, DOUGLAS W.	1957	1966
GROPIUS, WALTER	1968	1969	PERRY, WM. GRAVES.	1964	1975
GUGLER, ERIC	1946	1974	PLATT, CHAS. A.*	1911	1933
HARMON, ARTHUR L.	1944	1958	POPE, JOHN R.	1924	1937

	Elected	Died		Elected	Died
POST, GEORGE B.	1908	1913	THOMPSON, M. E.†	1826	1877
ROOT, JOHN W.	1955	1963	TOWN, ITHIEL†	1826	1844
SAARINEN, EERO	1958	1961	WALKER, RALPH	1949	1973
SAARINEN, ELIEL	1946	1950	WHITE, LAWRENCE G.	1948	1956
SHEPLEY, HENRY R.	1943	1962	WILLIAMS, EDGAR I.	1955	1974
SMITH, JAMES K.	1944	1961	WURSTER, WILLIAM W.	1962	1973
SWARTWOUT, E.	1934	1943	ZANTZINGER, C. C.	1945	1954

Workers in the Graphic Arts

	Elected	Died		Elected	Died
ANDERSON, ALEX.†	1826	1870	LINTON, WM. J.	1882	1897
ARMS, J. T.	1933	1953	LOZOWICK, LOUIS	1972	1973
CASTELLON, FEDERICO	1963	1971	MAIN, WILLIAM†	1826	1876
CHAMBERLAIN, SAMUEL	1945	1975	MAVERICK, PETER†	1826	1831
CHEFFETZ, ASA	1944	1965	MORGAN, WALLACE	1947	1948
COLE, TIMOTHY	1908	1931	NASON, THOMAS W.	1940	1971
DANFORTH, M. I.†	1826	1862	PENNELL, JOSEPH	1909	1926
DARLEY, F. O. C.	1852	1888	PRUD'HOMME, J. F.	1846	1892
DEHN, ADOLPH	1961	1968	REYNARD, GRANT T.	1963	1968
EBY, KERR	1934	1946	RIGGS, ROBERT	1946	1970
FABRI, RALPH	1946	1975	SCHULTHEISS, CARL M.	1946	1961
GIBSON, CHAS. D.	1932	1944	SMILLIE, JAMES	1851	1885
GRANT, GORDON	1947	1962	SPRUANCE, BENTON	1959	1967
HEINTZELMAN, A.	1937	1965	WICKEY, HARRY	1946	1968
JONES, ALFRED	1851	1900	WOLF, HENRY	1908	1916
KENT, NORMAN	1949	1972	WORTMAN, DENYS	1947	1958
LANDACRE, PAUL	1946	1963	WRIGHT, CHAS. C.†	1826	1854
LANKES, J. J.	1954	1960	WRIGHT, GEORGE	1939	1951
LEWIS, ALLEN	1935	1957			

Aquarellists

	Elected	Died		Elected	Died
BAUMGARTNER, W.	1950	1963	BURCHFIELD, CHARLES	1954	1967
BIGGS, WALTER	1947	1968	DELBOS, JULIUS	1948	1970

	Elected	Died		Elected	Died
HEITLAND, W. E.	1951	1969	O'HARA, ELIOT	1948	1969
KAUTZKY, T.	1950	1953	WHORF, JOHN	1947	1959
KOSA, EMIL J., JR.	1951	1968	WILLIAMS, JOHN A.	1947	1951
MILLER, BARSE	1947	1973			

Deceased Associates
(* Also a member of the Society of American Artists.)

Painters

	Elected	Died		Elected	Died
ALBEE, PERCY	1943	1959	BRECKENRIDGE, H. H.	1913	1937
ALBERT, ERNEST	1922	1946	BREDIN, R. SLOAN	1921	1933
ALLEN, THOMAS*	1884	1924	BRICHER, ALF. T.	1879	1908
ANSHUTZ, THOMAS	1910	1912	BRIDGES, FIDELIA	1873	1923
AUDUBON, J. W.	1840	1862	BRINLEY, D. P.	1930	1963
BAER, WILLIAM J.	1913	1941	BROWN, JOHN A.*	1896	1902
BAUM, WALTER E.	1945	1956	BROWNE, BELMORE	1928	1954
BEAL, REYNOLDS	1909	1951	BROWNE, CHAS. F.	1913	1920
BELL, E. A.*	1901	1953	BRUCE, EDWARD	1935	1943
BERNEKER, L. F.	1931	1937	BRUESTLE, GEO. M.	1927	1939
BERNINGHAUS, O. E.	1926	1952	BRYANT, HENRY	1837	1881
BICKNELL, F. A.	1913	1943	BUEHR, K. A.	1922	1952
BIRNEY, WM. V.	1900	1909	BUNNER, A. F.	1880	1897
BLONDELL, J. DE.	1854	1877	CARPENTER, F. B.	1852	1900
BLUMENSCHEIN, M. G.	1913	1958	CARRIGAN, WM. L.	1936	1939
BOGARDUS, MRS. M.	1845	1878	CASER, ETTORE	1931	1944
BOGERT, GEORGE H.*	1899	1944	CHAMPNEY, J. W.	1882	1903
BOLTON, WM. JAY	1845	1884	CHASE, ADELAIDE C.*	1906	1944
BORG, CARL OSCAR	1938	1947	CHASE, HARRY	1883	1889
BOSLEY, FRED A.	1931	1942	CLARKSON, RALPH	1910	1942
BOSTON, J. H.*	1901	1954	CLONNEY, JAS. G.	1834	1867
BOUTELLE, DE WITT C.	1852	1884	CLOVER, L. P., JR.	1840	1896
BRADFORD, F. S.	1932	1961	COHEN, LEWIS	1911	1915
BRADFORD, WILLIAM	1874	1892	COLEMAN, C. C.	1865	1928
BRANDEGEE, R. B.*	1907	1922	COLYER, VINCENT	1851	1888

	Elected	Died		Elected	Died
COMAN, C. B.	1910	1924	FULLER, GEORGE*	1853	1884
CORNOYER, PAUL	1909	1923	FULLER, HENRY B.*	1906	1934
COTTON, WILLIAM	1916	1958	FULLER, LUCIA F.*	1906	1924
COX, LOUISE*	1902	1945	GAERTNER, C. F.	1952	1952
CRAIG, THOS. B.	1897	1924	GAUGENGIGL, I. M.*	1906	1932
CRANCH, JOHN	1853	1891	GAULEY, R. D.	1908	1943
CROWNINSHIELD,F.	1905	1918	GENTH, L. M.	1908	1953
CUMMINGS, T. A.	1852	1859	GILBERT, ARTHUR HILL	1930	1970
CUSHING, H. G.*	1906	1916	GRAIN, FREDERICK	1836	c1879
DAVIDSON, GEORGE	1936	1965	GRAVES, ABBOTT	1926	1936
DAY, J. FRANCIS*	1906	1942	GRAY, MARY	1929	1964
DEAS, CHARLES	1839	1867	GREEN, FRANK R.	1897	1940
DE LUCE, PERCIVAL	1897	1914	GROSZ, GEORGE.	1950	1959
DERRICK, WM. R.	1922	1941	GROVER, OLIVER D.	1913	1927
DETWILLER, F. K.	1939	1953	HAGGIN, BEN ALI	1912	1951
DIX, CHAS. T.	1861	1873	HALE, PHILIP L.	1917	1931
DODGE, JOHN W.	1832	1893	HALL, FRED G.	1938	1946
DRAKE, WM. H.	1902	1926	HAMILTON, W. R.	1833	?
DUNSMORE, J. W.	1925	1945	HARPER, W. ST. JOHN	1892	1910
EARLE, L. C.	1897	1921	HARRIS, J. T.	1839	1863
EATON, CHAS. H.	1893	1901	HARVEY, GEORGE	1828	1878
EATON, JOS. ORIEL	1866	1875	HAYS, WM. JACOB	1852	1875
EVERGOOD, PHILIP	1971	1973	HAYS, WILLIAM J.	1909	1934
FANSHAW, S. R.	1841	1888	HILL, JOHN W.	1833	1879
FAXON, WM. B.*	1906	1941	HILLS, LAURA C.*	1906	1952
FERGUSON, H. A.	1884	1911	HITCHCOCK, GEO.	1909	1913
FISHER, ALANSON	1845	1884	HOEBER, ARTHUR	1909	1915
FITCH, JOHN LEE	1870	1895	HOFFMAN, HARRY	1930	1964
FLAGG, CHAS. N.	1909	1916	HOPE, JAMES	1871	1892
FOOTE, WILL H.	1910	1965	HOPKINS, JAMES R.	1921	1969
FOSTER, WILL	1929	1953	HOWS, JOHN A.	1862	1874
FRAZIER, KENNETH*	1906	1949	HUBBELL, HENRY S.*	1906	1949
FREER, FRED W.*	1887	1908	HUDSON, ERIC	1926	1932
FRENCH, FRANK	1922	1933	HYDE, WM. H.*	1900	1943
FROMKES, MAURICE	1927	1931	INMAN, J. O'BRIEN	1865	1896
FROTHINGHAM, S.	1845	1861	IRVINE, WILSON	1926	1936

	Elected	Died		Elected	Died
IRWIN, BENONI	1889	1896	MILLET, CLARENCE	1943	1959
JEWETT, WM.	1847	1874	MORGAN, WILLIAM	1862	1900
JEWETT, WM. S.	1845	1873	MOSCHCOWITZ, P.*	1906	1942
JONGERS, A.*	1906	1945	MOUNT, H. SMITH	1828	1841
KAPPES, ALFRED*	1887	1894	MULHAUPT, F.J.	1926	1938
KAYN, HILDE	1943	1950	NETTLETON, WALTER*	1905	1936
KEITH, DORA W.*	1906	1940	NEWCOMBE, G. W.	1832	1845
KELLER, HENRY	1939	1949	NICHOLS, ED. W.	1861	1871
KEYES, BERNARD M.	1938	1973	NIEMEYER, J. H.*	1906	1932
KIRK, FRANK C.	1944	1963	NIMS, JEREMIAH	1841	1841
KLINE, WM. F.	1901	1931	OAKLEY, GEORGE	1828	1869
KYLE, JOSEPH	1849	1863	ODDIE, WALTER M.	1833	1865
LANMAN, CHARLES	1842	1895	OGILVIE, CLINTON	1864	1900
LATHROP, FRANCIS*	1906	1909	PAGE, MARIE D.	1927	1940
LAY, OLIVER I.	1876	1890	PARKER, LAWTON S.	1916	1954
LAZARUS, JACOB H.	1849	1891	PARSONS, CHARLES	1862	1910
LEAKE, GERALD	1937	1975	PEARCE, CHAS. S.*	1906	1914
LOOMIS, CHESTER*	1906	1924	PEELE, JOHN T.	1846	1897
LOOP, MRS. H. A.	1873	1909	PEIXOTTO, ERNEST	1909	1940
LOW, MARY F.*	1906	1946	PHILIP, FRED W.	1833	1841
LYMAN, JOSEPH.	1886	1913	PICKNELL, WM. L.*	1891	1897
MAC CAMERON, R. L.	1910	1912	POORE, HENRY R.	1888	1940
MAC EWEN, W.	1903	1943	POPE, JOHN	1858	1880
MARCHANT, E. D.	1833	1887	POST, W. MERRITT	1910	1935
MARSH, FRED DANA	1906	1961	POWELL, WM. H.	1854	1879
MASON, MAUD M.	1934	1956	PRELLWITZ, E. M.*	1906	1944
MATTESON, T. H.	1847	1884	PRENDERGAST, CHAS.	1939	1948
MAY, EDW. H.	1849	1887	RAND, ELLEN E.	1926	1941
MAYER, CONSTANT	1866	1911	RANNEY, WM. T.	1850	1857
MC CORD, GEO. H.	1880	1909	REILLY, FRANK	1957	1967
MC ILHENNEY, C. M.	1892	1904	REINHARDT, B. F.	1871	1885
MEAKIN, LOUIS H.	1913	1917	REINHARDT, C. S.*	1891	1896
MECHAU, FRANK	1937	1946	REMINGTON, FRED	1891	1909
MEGAREY, JOHN	1844	1845	RICE, WM. M. J.*	1900	1922
MEIERE, HILDRETH	1942	1961	ROLSHOVEN, JULIUS	1926	1930
MELCARTH, EDWARD	1970	1973	RONDELL, FRED	1861	1892

	Elected	Died		Elected	Died
ROULAND, O.	1936	1945	TORREY, M. C.	1833	1837
RYDER, PLATT P.	1868	1896	TOWNSEND, ERNEST	1941	1945
RYLAND, ROBERT K.	1940	1951	TYLER, G. W.	1832	1833
SAINTIN, JULES E.	1861	1894	ULRICH, CHAS. F.*	1883	1908
SARTAIN, WILLIAM*	1880	1924	VINCENT, H. A.	1920	1931
SATTERLEE, WALTER	1879	1908	VOLKERT, EDW. C.	1921	1935
SCHREYVOGEL, C.	1901	1912	VOLLMERING, JOS.	1853	1887
SCHWARZ, FRANK H.	1934	1951	WALLCOTT, H. M.*	1903	1944
SCOTT, JULIAN	1870	1901	WALTMAN, HARRY F.	1917	1951
SERPELL, SUSANA W.	1912	1913	WARREN, A. W.	1863	1873
SEWELL, A. B.	1903	1926	WEBB, J. LOUIS*	1906	1928
SEWELL, R. V. V.	1901	1924	WEINEDEL, CARL	1839	1845
SHERWOOD, R. E.*	1906	1948	WENDT, WILLIAM	1912	1946
SMITH, THOS. L.	1869	1884	WETHERILL, E. K. K.	1927	1929
SPEAR, ARTHUR P.	1920	1959	WHITTEMORE, WM. J.	1897	1955
STEELE, THEO. C.	1913	1926	WIGHTMAN, THOS.	1849	1888
STORY, GEO. H.	1875	1922	WILLIAMSON, JOHN	1861	1885
STORY, JULIAN R.*	1906	1919	WILSON, MATTHEW	1843	1892
SWAIN, WM.	1836	1847	WITT, JOHN H.	1885	1901
TALBOT, JESSE	1845	1879	WOELFLE, A. W.	1929	1936
THOMPSON, C. G.	1861	1888	WOTHERSPOON, W. W.	1848	1888
THOMPSON, J.	1851	1886	WUST, ALEXANDER	1861	1876
THOMPSON, THOS.	1834	1852	YOUNG, CHARLES MORRIS	1913	1964
THORNDIKE, G. Q.	1861	1886			

Sculptors

	Elected	Died		Elected	Died
BORGLUM, S. H.	1911	1922	FIELDS, MITCHELL.	1945	1966
BOYLE, JOHN J.	1910	1917	JONES, THOMAS D.	1853	1881
BURROUGHS, MRS. E.	1913	1916	JOSSET, RAOUL	1953	1957
CAMDEN, HARRY P.	1942	1943	KALISH, MAX	1933	1945
CAVALLITO, ALBINO	1958	1966	KUNTZE, EDW. J.	1869	1870
CLARKE, THOS. S.	1902	1920	LASCARI, HILDA K.	1935	1937
DAVIDSON, JO.	1944	1952	LOPEZ, CHARLES A.*	1906	1906
EBERLE, A. ST. LEGER	1920	1942	LUKEMAN, A.	1909	1935

	Elected	Died		Elected	Died
MAC LEARY, BONNIE	1930	1971	PRATT, BELA L.	1910	1917
MALDARELLI, ORONZIO	1956	1963	QUINN, E. T.	1920	1929
MARTINY, PHILIP*	1902	1927	ROSIN, HARRY	1970	1973
NEWMAN, A. G.	1926	1940	RICCI, ULYSSES	1942	1960
O'DONOVAN, W. R.*	1878	1920	SCUDDER, JANET	1920	1940
PADDOCK, WILLARD	1922	1956	SHRADY, H. M.	1909	1922
PARK, MADELEINE	1960	1960	SPICER-SIMSON, T.	1951	1959
POLLIA, JOSEPH	1953	1954	WHITNEY, G. V.	1940	1942

Architects

	Elected	Died		Elected	Died
ARMSTRONG, D. M.*	1906	1918	HOWELLS, JOHN M.	1944	1959
ARMSTRONG, HARRIS	1972	1973	HOYT, BURNHAM	1953	1960
BARBER, DONN	1923	1925	JACKSON, F. ELLIS	1947	1950
BELLOWS, ROBERT P.	1956	1957	KAHN, LOUIS F.	1965	1974
BLAKE, THEODORE E.	1948	1949	KEBBON, ERIC	1952	1964
BORING, WM. A.	1913	1937	KLAUDER, CHAS. Z.	1938	1938
BRINCKERHOFF, A. R.	1948	1959	KOCH, RICHARD	1958	1971
BROWN, GLENN	1927	1932	KOHN, ROBERT D.	1953	1953
BUTLER, CHARLES	1953	1953	LA FARGE, C. G.	1910	1938
COLLENS, CHARLES	1953	1956	LITCHFIELD, E. D.	1951	1952
CRAM, R. A.	1938	1942	MAGONIGLE, H. V. B.	1924	1935
CROSS, JOHN WALTER	1942	1951	MARTIN, SYDNEY E.	1962	1970
DAILEY, G. A.	1956	1967	MURPHY, FRED V.	1951	1958
DAVIS, ALEX J.	1827	1892	NEUTRA, RICHARD J.	1964	1970
DAY, FRANK M.	1910	1918	PEABODY, ROBT. S.	1910	1917
GARFIELD, ABRAM	1949	1958	SNYDER, ELDREDGE	1965	1967
GEHRON, WILLIAM	1953	1958	TOOMBS, HENRY JOHNSTON	1951	1967
GEIFFERT, ALFRED, JR.	1951	1957	TROWBRIDGE, S. B. P.	1913	1925
GILBERT, CASS, JR.	1932	1975	VAN ALEN, WILLIAM	1943	1954
GITHENS, ALFRED M.	1948	1973	WALKER, C. H.	1911	1936
GREENLEAF, J. L.	1924	1933	WALKER, C. W.	1952	1967
HARDENBERGH, H. J.	1910	1918	WHEELWRIGHT, R.	1952	1965
HIRONS, FRED C.	1932	1942	WRIGHT, FRANK L.	1952	1959
HOWARD, JOHN G.	1910	1931	WOODBRIDGE, FREDERICK J.	1953	1974
HOWE, GEORGE	1951	1955			

Workers in the Graphic Arts

	Elected	Died
ADAMS, JOSEPH A.	1833	1880
BACHER, OTTO H.*	1906	1909
BENDINER, ALFRED	1964	1964
BOTTS, HUGH	1942	1964
BULLER, CECIL	1949	1974
CHENEY, S. W.	1848	1856
DALLAS, JACOB A.	1854	1857
DANIEL, LEWIS C.	1948	1952
DEINES, E. HUBERT	1943	1967
FAWCETT, ROBERT	1964	1967
GREATOREX, ELIZA	1869	1897
HAVENS, JAMES D.	1951	1960
HELLER, HELEN WEST	1948	1955
HUNTLEY, VICTORIA HUTSON	1942	1971
HURLEY, E. T.	1948	1950
KINNEY, TROY	1933	1938

	Elected	Died
LIMBACH, RUSSELL T.	1952	1971
MACK, WARREN B.	1944	1952
MAC LAUGHLAN, D. S.	1935	1938
MASON, ABRAHAM	1830	1884
MASTRO-VALERIO, A.	1951	1953
MC CORMICK, H.	1928	1943
MIELATZ, C. F. W.	1906	1919
MUELLER, HANS	1948	1962
MURPHY, ALICE H.	1949	1966
OBERHARDT, WM.	1945	1958
PARADISE, J. W.	1833	1862
PETERSEN, MARTIN	1943	1956
WASHBURN, C.	1940	1965
WATT, WM. G.	1922	1924
WILSON, EDWARD A.	1949	1970

Aquarellists

	Elected	Died
AIKEN, CHARLES A.	1962	1965
DE MAINE, HARRY	1951	1952
GANNAM, JOHN.	1950	1965

	Elected	Died
OLSEN, HERBERT	1951	1973
QUACKENBUSH, LARRY	1967	1967
RIPLEY, A. LASSELL	1954	1969

Honorary Members

Prior to 1863 the Academy elected honorary members, artists not residing in New York were then ineligible for regular membership. Among these honorary members were:

AGATE, ALFRED
Washington, D. C.   *Painter*   1840

ALEXANDER, FRANCIS
Florence   *Painter*   1839

ALLSTON, WASHINGTON, ARA
Boston   *Painter*   1827

AUDUBON, JOHN JAMES
New York   *Ornithologist, Artist*   1833

BIRCH, THOMAS
Philadelphia   *Painter*   1833

BULFINCH, CHARLES
Washington, D. C.   *Architect*   1827

CATHERWOOD, FREDERICK
Demerara   *Architect*   1837

CHENEY, JOHN
Boston   *Engraver*   1833

CORNELIUS, PETER VON
Germany   *Painter*   1845

CRAWFORD, THOMAS
Rome   *Sculptor*   1838

DAGUERRE, LOUIS JACQUES MANDE
Paris   *Painter*   1839

DE LA ROCHE, PAUL HIPPOLYTE
Paris   *Painter*   1845

DOUGHTY, THOMAS
New York   *Painter*   1827

EASTLAKE, SIR CHARLES LOCK, PRA
London   *Painter*   1845

FISHER, ALVAN
Boston   *Painter*   1827

GIBSON, JOHN
Rome   *Sculptor*   1833

GREENOUGH, HORATIO
Rome   *Sculptor*   1828

HARDING, CHESTER
Boston   *Painter*   1828

HAVILAND, JOHN
Philadelphia   *Architect*   1827

HEALY, GEORGE PETER ALEXANDER
Rome   *Painter*   1843

HOPPIN, THOMAS FREDERICK
Providence   *Illustrator*   1844

HUGHES, PROFESSOR BALL, NAD
Boston   *Sculptor*   1830

KEYSER, NICAISE DE, DRA
Antwerp   *Painter*   1846

LAMBDIN, JAMES R., DPAFA
Philadelphia   *Painter*   1839

LAWRENCE, SIR THOMAS, PRA
London   *Painter*   1827

LESLIE, CHARLES ROBERT, RA
London   *Painter*   1827

LIVINGSTON, MONTGOMERY   *Painter*   1847

MORGHEN, RAPHAEL
Florence   *Engraver*   1830

NEAGLE, JOHN
Philadelphia   *Painter*   1828

NEWTON, GILBERT STUART, ARA
England   *Painter*   1827

PALMER, ERASTUS DOW
   Albany, N. Y.   *Sculptor* 1849

PEALE, ROSALBA
   Philadelphia   *Painter* 1828

POWERS, HIRAM
   Florence   *Sculptor* 1837

RETZCH, F. A. MORITZ
   Dresden   *Illustrator* 1836

ROTHERMEL, PETER FREDERICK
   Philadelphia   *Painter* 1837

SARGENT, COL. HENRY
   Boston   *Painter* 1840

STRICKLAND, WILLIAM
   Philadelphia   *Architect* 1827

STUART, GILBERT
   Boston   *Painter* 1827

SULLY, JANE
   Philadelphia   *Painter* 1830

SULLY, THOMAS
   Philadelphia   *Painter* 1827

THORVALDSEN, CAV. ALBERT BERTEL
   Copenhagen   *Sculptor* 1829

VERNET, EMILIE JEAN HORACE
   Paris   *Painter* 1845

WAPPERS, E. C. GUSTAVE, BARON
   Antwerp   *Painter* 1833

WATSON, STUART
   Edinboro, N. Y.   *Painter* 1858

WAUGH, SAMUEL B.
   Janesville, Wisconsin   *Painter* 1847

Honorary Corresponding Members

(* Deceased)

ANNIGONI, PIETRO   *Italy* 1959

BESNARD, ALBERT*   *Paris* 1932

BLOMFIELD, SIR REGINALD*
   (Architect)   *London* 1933

BONNAT, LEON*   *Paris* 1917

CASSON, ALFRED JOSEPH, PRCA
   (Painter)   *Canada* 1952

FLAMENG, FRANCO*   *Paris* 1919

GREBER, JACQUES*
   (Architect)   *Paris* 1962

GRIER, SIR WYLY, PRCA*   *Canada* 1937

JANNIOT, ALFRED
   (Sculptor)   *Paris* 1959

KELLY, SIR GERALD, PRA   *London* 1950

LALOUX, VICTOR*
   (Architect)   *Paris* 1932

MONNINGTON, SIR THOMAS, PRA   *London* 1975

PARKIN, JOHN C., PRCA
   (Architect)   *Canada* 1972

PILOT, ROBERT W., PRCA   *Canada* 1952

POYNTER, SIR EDWARD J.*   *London* 1917

ROLL, ALFRED*   *Paris* 1919

ROMANELLI, ROMANO
   (Sculptor)   *Italy* 1933

SCOTT, SIR GILES GILBERT*
   (Architect)   *London* 1950

WEBB, SIR T. ASTON*   *London* 1919

WHEELER, SIR CHARLES, PRA
   (Sculptor)   *London* 1958

ZULOAGA Y ZANORA, IGNACIO*   *Spain* 1933

Fellows for Life

The contribution or devise of five hundred dollars in cash, securities or property shall render the donor eligible to be elected or declared a Fellow for Life of the National Academy of Design by the President and Council

This class is now open.
It is requested that the Secretary be notified promptly in case of death or of any change of address.

ABRAMOVITZ, MAX, NA

BACHE, MRS. ALICE

BARTEL, EWALD

BENEDICT, JAMES

BENSON, BERNHARD

BLOCH, THADDENE

CLEMENS, MRS. JAMES B.

COOPER, DR. HENRY

DAVIES, J. CLARENCE

DEITSCH, SAMUEL L.

DE LAITTRE, MRS. KARL

EGAN, MRS. ELOISE

EPSTEIN, NAT

FORD, MRS. GERALD R.

FRICK, MISS HELEN CLAY

GARDINER, MISS SARAH D.

HARRISON, RICHARD C.

HARRISON, WALLACE K., NA

HOVING, THOMAS P. F.

JONES, MRS. A. S. H.

LITT, SOLOMON

MAITLAND, ROBERT L.

MOORE, JOSEPH T.

MOTT, HOPPER LENOX

NOBLE, JOSEPH VEACH

PARKIN, WILLIAM

POOR, ALFRED EASTON, PNA

RHOADES, MISS C. HARSEN

SALZBRENNER, ALBERT

SAMSTAG, H. ROBERT

TAYLOR, DR. JOSHUA C.

THIRY, PAUL, NA

TRAIN, MRS. HELEN COSTER

YOUNG, THEODORE J., ANA

By courtesy
Wives of Presidents of National Academy of Design

MRS. ELIOT CLARK

MRS. DEWITT M. LOCKMAN

MRS. ALFRED EASTON POOR

MRS. LAWRENCE GRANT WHITE

MRS. EDGAR I. WILLIAMS

Fellows in Perpetuity

The contribution or devise of One Thousand Dollars in cash, securities or property shall render the donor eligible to be elected or declared a Fellow in Perpetuity of the National Academy of Design by the President and Council. Holders of Fellowships shall have no vote in the management of the Academy. They shall receive a Diploma carrying the Seal of the Academy and invitations to all social gatherings and openings.

A Fellow in Perpetuity shall be entitled to convey his Fellowship to an heir or assignee and the holder of the Diploma shall enjoy the privilege of the original subscriber.

ADAMS, KEMPTON*

AGAR, JOHN G.*

ARTHUR, MRS. GEORGE D.

BACON, FRANCIS M., JR.

BARBEY, PIERRE LORILLARD, JR.

BROWN, JOHN CROSBY

BROWN, MRS. THOMAS MCKLEE

BURR, MR. CHARLES P.

BUTLER, HOWARD RUSSELL, JR.

BUTTOLPH, DAVID L.

CLARKE, GILMORE D., NA

CONSTABLE, JAMES M.

COXE, REGINALD CLEVELAND*

DENNY, THOMAS*

DILLON, DOUGLAS

DOWS, DAVID

DUDLEY, MISS LAURA FELLOWS

ETTL, ALEXANDER J.

FAULKNER, WALDRON, ANA

FRIEDSAM, COL. MICHAEL*

FRY, JOHN HEMING*

GANDY, MISS KATHERINE

GERRY, MRS. ROBERT L.*

HERMAN, HELEN STARR

HOE, EDWARD LIVINGSTON

HOE, ROBERT, 4TH

HUNTINGTON, ARCHER M.*

HURLBUT, MRS. MARGARET H.

JOHNSON, DOROTHY AIKEN

JONES, MRS. LORING P.

KOCH, JOHN, NA

KOCHERTHALER, MINA

KOSA, MRS. EMIL J., JR.

LANG, MRS. HENRY*

LAURENCE, MRS. ALICE JEROME*

LEARNED, EDWARD KERNOCHAN

LOVETT, MRS. ADELE BROWN

LOW, A. AUGUSTUS*

LOWTHER, MRS. MILLIE RADER*

MELLON, ELEANOR, NA

MILLER, DR. GEORGE NORTON

MOFFAT, ABBOT LOW

MORGAN, MRS. ALEX C.

MORRIS, HARRISON S.*

NAUGHTON, MRS. F. P.

NEUBERGER, ROY

OLYPHANT, DAVID

ORR, DOUGLAS W., NA*

PARISH, JR., MRS. EDWARD C.

PARSONS, MRS. J. RUSSELL

PELL, HERBERT C., III

RAPUANO, MICHAEL, NA

REESE, MRS. S. M. PAGE

SHELDON, EDWIN B.*

STILLMAN, CHARLES C.

THORNE, OAKLEIGH

THORNE, SAMUEL*

VANDERBILT, MRS. CORNELIUS*

VAN DER VOORT, AMANDA

VON HESSE, MRS. EMILY

WARBURG, FELIX M.*

WATSON, THOMAS J.*

WEBB, MRS. SAMUEL B.

WEEMS, KATHARINE LANE, NA

WEILER, DR. RALPH*

WETMORE, SARAH TAYLOR*

WHITING, DR. FREDERICK L.

WIGGINS, CARLETON, II

WILLIAMS, JOHN S.

WRIGHT, CHARLES LENNOX

WRIGHT, CATHARINE MORRIS, NA

(* Deceased)

Gifts and Bequests

Gifts and bequests to the National Academy of Design are deductible for the purpose of computing income, gift and inheritance taxes under the laws of New York State and of the United States to the extent provided in those laws as to donations and bequests to educational corporations.

A contribution of $50,000 or more shall constitute the donor a Benefactor.

A contribution of $25,000 shall constitute the donor a Patron.

A contribution of $10,000 shall constitute the donor a Sustainer.

A contribution of $5,000 shall constitute the donor a Donor.

A contribution of $1,500 shall constitute the donor a Contributor.

The Benefactors, Patrons, Sustainers, Donors, and Contributors shall be entitled to such rights and benefits as may be from time to time decided by the Council.

Sustainers

PRISCILLA MAXWELL ENDICOTT

MURRAY KUPFERMAN

Donor

WILLIAM P. SCHWEITZER

Contributors

MRS. DUNBAR BOSTWICK

RALPH FABRI, N.A.*

OLIVER R. GRACE

JOHN F. HARBESON, N.A.

DOUGLAS W. ORR, N.A.*

DAGMAR H. TRIBBLE

LILA ACHESON WALLACE

CHI-CHUAN WANG

*Deceased